THE POPULATION AHEAD

∞   ∞   ∞   ∞   ∞   ∞   ∞

THE

∞ # POPULATION ∞   ∞   ∞

AHEAD

∞   ∞   ∞   ∞   ∞   ∞   ∞

∞   ∞   ∞   *edited by Roy G. Francis*   ∞

∞   ∞   ∞   ∞   ∞   ∞   ∞

∞   ∞   ∞   ∞   ∞   ∞   ∞

UNIVERSITY OF MINNESOTA PRESS *Minneapolis*

——————————————————————————— ∞

Foreword

DURING the last decade many faculty members of the University of Minnesota have interested themselves deeply in the study of human population, not only as part of the substance of the day-to-day inquiries common to academicians but also as an effort to provide for a generation perplexed about its future the most comprehensive classification of social-science subjects or "problems" under which that future may be considered. The interest of these faculty members, reinforced by a kindred interest among members of the Human Genetics League, led in 1948 to the first population conference, specifically titled "Symposium on Populations and Relationships between Groups," and held at the Center for Continuation Study of the university in November 1948.

At the time of the 1948 symposium the recent period of worldwide population-rate increase had hardly begun, and by many students of demographic phenomena such increases as had been noted were taken as natural correctives to the depletion of the war years immediately preceding. There was a tendency to believe (at least in countries of Western civilization) that such a postwar flare-up would soon subside, that in most urbanized areas of the world limiting factors identified before the end of the war would again take over, and that population history would again proceed along the line of Pearl's curve. There was also a general belief that this would not be true of many of the un-urbanized or underdeveloped areas of the earth, and the students of population were therefore preoccupied with the probable results of the contrasting net rates of increase in the two classes of population groups.

This preoccupation showed itself in the plan of procedure of the 1948 symposium, which consisted, first, of a presentation of the facts

v

about worldwide population growth in modern times, and second, of a consideration of population phenomena in several selected areas of the earth — areas illustrative of different cultural, racial, economic, and political factors believed to be significant and important. For this purpose the university assembled a notable group of experts in various disciplines professionally concerned with inquiries of such a nature.

Viewed from the winter of 1957, the 1948 symposium seems to have placed almost all its emphasis upon quantitative considerations, bringing into its discussions other elements of human experience mainly as they might bear upon the ultimate net rates of increase among humankind. There were some exceptions, to be sure, but it seems clear that in 1948, cowering before the bogeyman of prospective failure of the food supply and of other resources, the group attending the symposium might have summarized its discussions by the question "What can be done to bring about a selective restriction of population growth?"

These matters are mentioned as a sort of prelude to the 1957 conference because they point up significant changes in the approach of students of population during the intervening years. The bogeyman of shortage is still with us, of course, but there is a much more general optimistic feeling that we have effective charms against him. And the former absorbing preoccupation with mere numbers has changed to a more searching and more tolerant inquiry as to the qualities that will prove desirable in the numbers we breed, both on the physiological and on the cultural side.

Such changes of attitude became apparent in the preliminary planning of the program of the 1957 symposium, which was held at the Center for Continuation Study under the title "The Second Symposium on Population Problems." The conference may be briefly described as a discussion from the point of view of a number of subject fields of the factors that are pertinent to a definition of an "optimum" population. It became apparent almost at once that what might be called relativistic attitudes forbade an attempt to settle upon any one such definition. Almost every point of view tended to create its own concept of "optimum," and the first inquiry came to be "optimum for *what*?"

The plan of the symposium is well revealed by the contents of this volume, but a brief word of explanation may be in order. The program began with a review of the 1948 meeting, and the introduction of data to bring the world-population situation up to date. Following this basic analysis and summary, specialists in several disciplines provided relevant information indicating what optimum concept might arise out of the background of researches and findings from their own fields of study. These disciplines and the rationale of their selection are well described by Professor Francis in the introduction (pages 3–11). The presentations by the several specialists were followed by discussions, in the course of which important supplementary comments were made. These discussions could not be reproduced in full, but they have been partially digested and partially reproduced in the chapter "Commentary" (pages 125–51).

As Professor Francis explains in his introduction, the specialists who were assembled for the symposium were urged to forswear the technical jargon of their disciplines and to use the colloquial speech of the rest of us. In spite of their willingness to do this, and their attempts to comply with the request, many of us will find parts of their exposition rather hard going, not because of the failure of the speakers, but because of our own unfamiliarity with the type of study in which they are engaged. This is, however, truly a blessing in disguise if it leads citizens of this nation to personal study in many directions vital to the welfare of their country and their posterity, for they will be called upon to make decisions of tremendous consequence on these issues.

The Second Symposium on Population Problems was made possible by financial assistance from the Population Council, Incorporated, and from the Minnesota Human Genetics League. The university and those who attended the conference have expressed warm appreciation for this help. The university and its Center for Continuation Study also wish to express thanks to all who participated as specialists and commentators in the symposium, and to those who served on the committee to plan for the event. Special thanks are heartily extended to Professor Roy Francis, who has served as editor of this book and contributor thereto.

J. M. NOLTE
DEAN, GENERAL EXTENSION DIVISION
UNIVERSITY OF MINNESOTA

Center for Continuation Study
April 11, 1957

The Population Ahead

Commentary, BY Warren S. Thompson, DIRECTOR EMERITUS, SCRIPPS FOUNDATION FOR RESEARCH IN POPULATION PROBLEMS, 125; Philip M. Raup, PROFESSOR OF AGRICULTURAL ECONOMICS, UNIVERSITY OF MINNESOTA, 130; Sheldon Reed, DIRECTOR, DIGHT INSTITUTE, UNIVERSITY OF MINNESOTA, 135; Alex Weingrod, INSTRUCTOR IN ANTHROPOLOGY, UNIVERSITY OF MINNESOTA, 138; Dwight Minnich, CHAIRMAN, DEPARTMENT OF ZOOLOGY, UNIVERSITY OF MINNESOTA, 148

Errata

Before the release of this volume, the following errors were discovered. The editor regrets that they appear in the text and wishes to acknowledge that he alone is responsible for them.

Pages 66–68, beginning with line 26 and continuing to the bottom of page 68, all references to calories should be capitalized. For calories read Calories

Page 67, line 6, for he would consume essentially all the carnivory read he would require essentially all the carnivory

Page 67, line 15, last column, for Production in Calories per Square Meter per Year read Production in Kilocalories per Square Meter per Year

Page 71, lines 19–25, substitute the following (continuing the sentence beginning on line 17, "The trouble is that an 'S' curve of this kind 'fits,' or describes, one set of data but"): does so no better than does a mathematically different "S" curve. Fitting curves to data is deceptively easy, and lays a trap for those who are unwilling (or worse, unable) to test their assumptions empirically. Our problem is people (or animals), not assumptions, and we make progress faster by studying births and deaths separately, first as related to population density and then as related to each other. This is what experimental ecologists have been doing.

Page 71, line 28, for equal to read a way of; for any read one

Page 71, line 31, for the population of the preceding population read numerical size of the preceding population

∞

Table of Contents

THE POPULATION AHEAD

———————————————————————————— ∞

The Desegregation of Ideas

MODERN man, collectively, knows more than he thinks he does. Man, the individual, shares the collective knowledge of mankind; but no individual shares it all, and, however curious he may be, if he submits to a formal learning process he soon finds it easier to be well versed in comparatively little than to try to embrace a comprehensive universalism. Since the path to learning is usually the path to specialization, it is the one most men follow. The expert, therefore, is difficult to replace — either in a conversation or in the preliminaries to effective action. In our modern civilization, although the generalist is often valuable, the specialist is indispensable.

But there are penalties attached to the development of the specialist. In the task of setting up the specifications of the expert, barriers arise. Certain "problem areas" tend to be pre-empted by various "fields" or "disciplines." Encroachments by the apostles of one discipline upon the territory of another tend to be resisted. Under the guise of academic disputation, jurisdictional controversies arise whenever an interloper is discovered. Partly because common language is ambiguous, "means all things to all men," and partly because of factors involving prestige, each discipline tends to develop its own vocabulary. This, in turn, furnishes further aid in maintaining intellectual empires. For none but those admitted to the new priesthood can understand what the intra-disciplinary discussions are all about. Thus intellectualism sets itself apart from humanity-in-general. And the man in the street — the poor docile character who pays for all this in the blind hope that his sacrifice will lead to a better world — is left far, far behind.

In some respects, indeed, this segregation of the disciplines is the

3

father of the evil; for if the various "experts" deride each other, upon whom is the average citizen to found his faith? Historically, the citizen has given his allegiance to whoever wooed him with declarations of tenderest love. And this very fact has in itself been dismaying to the expert, devoted as he must be, as a professional, to the objective pursuit of truth. The experts have asked, "Why has the world's path not led to the door of the laboratory?" They have not realized that their own bickering over better mousetraps has barred the path and even locked the laboratory door.

But looking at the matter honestly, and with due reverence to the discoveries of the specialists, one must concede that sociology is not psychology, nor is either of them identical with (although both are closely related to) anthropology. And none of these is, exactly, geography or economics. And how about genetics? Of course not. Indeed, if you want the truth of the matter, the barriers separating such disciplines are high. Protective tariffs abound.

Let us make it plain that most participants in these disciplines are unhappy about this state of affairs. They realize that the scientist has a moral responsibility to the society in which he lives. They deprecate the barriers and feel that there must be earnest attempts at desegregation. Such a term, to be sure, is not used: in today's lexicon one "segregates" on the basis of skin color, not of academic hue. Addicted to a vocabulary suitable for philosophizing, they prefer to state the goal thus: "We ought to work toward an integration of the social sciences."

To this noble sentiment the common citizen says Amen! and even Huzzah! But, pray tell, how is this integration going to occur? Will some super-intellectual create an empire extending over all the now independent states? The recent experience of the natural sciences indicates that the question ought not to be taken lightly.

In fact there have been and there are now in progress various attempts at integrating man's knowledge. History has taught us to expect, occasionally, the encyclopedic person who agglomerates all loose-ended information within the confines of his skull. And the more erudite of these synthesizers have transmitted this information to the printed page. But man-in-the-mass, in spite of the testimony of the quiz programs on television, has been reluctant to leave integration to the encyclopedia. He has been even more reluctant to fashion his own ideas of integration from any deliberate and pedestrian compendium. The

4

latter remains to him an indigestible digest of a more or less interesting body of knowledge. He says, "So what?" and will have none of it.

There have been other attempts rather more audacious in character. The initial starting places have been more lofty, and by their very altitude they have ruled out most of us. To us they are builded in the stratosphere of intellectual argument. Few can thrive in this rarefied atmosphere, and all but those endowed with special mental constitutions find it difficult to breathe.

One must be careful not to belittle too much this type of integration. However limited our comprehension of the substance of this recondite knowledge, we are nevertheless patiently aware of the need to formulate a precise terminology — a vocabulary which can be shared by a variety of points of view. But we wonder if this is in truth where integration begins. We feel dismayed to think that the major obstacle to integration is a barrier of words. We realize that these different word-systems were designed to fit the requirements of their respective disciplines, and that they have been useful in this connection; but, following Stuart Mill at a humble and respectful distance, we wonder whether the words are or can ever be responsive to the realities implicit in integration, whether what seems to us a possible conceptual disparity is not actually more basic than the difficulty of finding the right set of words.

From this angle, a concept is not merely a set of letters arranged in an arbitrary manner. A concept represents a point of view. As points of view differ, so does the object being studied. As long as the object appears to be different to different observers, little can be done by way of integration if the latter requires that we all look at the world in precisely the same manner.

There are at least two more ways of working on the problem of integrating several points of view. Both of these have found haven at the University of Minnesota, as well as at other major universities in the land. One of these is to draw scholars together, not for the sake of reconciling vocabularies, but to share research experience, to partake of the theory, vocabulary, and data of a variety of disciplines. In this process there is no a priori notion of what "integration" is going to be, or even if it is possible. If nothing else results, at least barriers will come down; these scholars will be able to move freely from one discipline to another. This in itself is no small achievement. If the process

5

entails a number of faltering steps, the final goal seems surely to justify them.

The final way of approaching the possibility of integration is a corollary of the preceding, and is that used in gathering the material in this volume. It includes the assembling of representatives of various disciplines, but in this case a specific *problem area* is defined — in the present instance, *population*. Out of the problem area one special task is designated: What must be taken into account in thinking of an "optimum" population, or of "optimum population growth"?

Well, many disciplines regard people intently. For example, the medical researcher observes the human body and theorizes about it. In considering man as a biological specimen, what relation is there between his food intake and his expectancy of life? This question — how long can a man survive — is not a small issue. One of our basic premises is the love of life. We avoid death; even its discussion is often taboo. We wish and strive to remove physical suffering and the want that often causes it. In speaking of a "social class," a social scientist often refers to the different claims people have on the rewards in life — and we commonly observe a "wealthy upper class" who have superior claims (through money and position) on Cadillacs, vacations in Europe, and so on. But what about the claim on life itself? If one class can live longer than another, on the average or in the aggregate, is this not an important difference? Consequently, in studying population, we must listen to the medical profession.

But a human being is not a mere accumulation of biological tissues. His "problem" is not solely that of biological survival. For one thing, man lives almost everywhere on the face of the earth. Sometimes we may be hard put to explain why anyone would want to live where he does. Moreover, some areas have more people than others. Some groups of people live by agriculture, others by industry, and so on. The geographic distribution of man and, indeed, the relation between man and the land he occupies pose many interesting questions.

Some time ago a writer wrote a story trying to answer the query "How much land does a man require?" The answer still eludes us. Certainly the nomadic hunter or gatherer of foods needs more acreage than does an animal or plant husbandman. The geographer, who deals with such considerations, is thus properly interested in population and must become one of our consultative team.

In observing that men live differently, we have noticed that characteristically they live in groups, and that this process of group living brings problems not entirely within the province of the geographer. A population is not merely an assembly of individuals. The individuals composing it are related in various ways. The sociologist, a scientist who is keenly aware of social relations — of what we call "society" — and of the consequences such relations have upon behavior, is keenly interested in population. Does the size of a social group indicate how it is to be organized? Does the rate of change of population growth or decline affect the policy-making aspects of a society? What is the relation, say, between attitudes toward children and the birth rate? What relation exists between religious ideology, as such, and family size? Or between urbanism as a way of life and family size? What relation exists between farming and attitudes toward children? These are sociological questions, the answers to which immediately affect what we know and believe about population. The sociologist must therefore also be invited to join our body of experts.

Our search rapidly takes us even further. Man's societies exist in a cultural matrix, a sort of mold or bed of artifacts and traditions out of his past. "Culture" and "society," although they have common elements, are not equivalent terms. "Society" refers to people and their relations. "Culture" refers to the things of life — the tools, ideas, habits, equipment, lore, all the learned parts of living together. Of course one's culture affects the population. What of those whose ideology justifies infanticide? What of the tradition of birth control, or the tradition of denying mechanical birth control? The student of these matters (among others) in human groups of all kinds and in all places is the anthropologist, and he has much to say about population, and about changes in rates of growth.

Another rather specific part of man's culture worthy of intense study is the set of behaviors and related artifacts associated with making a living — the economic system. In any consideration of economic behavior, to be sure, social relations are interwoven. The entrepreneur is not "independent" of his employees. The foreman does not exist apart from the work gang. The buyer buys from a seller. And yet, there is clearly an element of the problem that relates to the way in which man uses the land for his living.

If the average American looks around him, he sees an extremely high standard of living. He sees a continuous and increasing parade of automobiles, newer, longer, heavier. He views this " ` pride. Constantly he seeks new things — clothing, house furnishings, washing machines, automatic dryers, mechanical refrigerators, stoves — things for the home and elsewhere. He views all this with pride. Life is a wonderful cornucopia.

Some people, however, wonder about how the supply of materials is holding out. Annually we increase the rate of depletion of many natural resources. Will we be able to continue this pace of consuming basic materials? Now suppose that the peoples with a less generous standard of living were given one equal to ours: how much more of a strain would there be on the resources of the world? How much more steel would we consume? How much more petroleum? Electricity?

Suppose that the rest of the world were to look at us and wonder, is the United States consuming too much? What obligations do we have to the rest of mankind — those in other areas, those yet to come? How many more people can the world support? The purely economic question, as well as those that are more peripheral, such as proper land utilization, must be discussed if we are to speak of population intelligently.

Some time ago, high school students were feverishly debating the subject of "heredity versus environment" as *the* explanation of behavior. We have since learned to replace the word "versus" with the word "and" and read it "heredity and environment." This exchange in words has been slow in coming, and there are still those who dislike the obligation of admitting hereditary factors. The basic reason, one suspects, is that a number of people fear that the admission of heredity *implies* a racist doctrine. No such implication is present. To admit that there are such things as idiots, imbeciles, and morons in no way suggests that any race is free from such deficiencies. So most of us are willing to acknowledge certain factors of physical constitution in trying to determine at least some limits of human experience.

Alas! In so doing, have we not opened Pandora's box? How do we set these limits? What are the genetic probabilities, in respect to the qualitative aspects of population? Moreover, in view of some recent comments on the adverse effects of radiation, how much need we fear for the genetic future? Are our children likely to breed a generation of monsters? To understand the scope of the population problem, ques-

8

tions about quantity are obviously insufficient. The geneticist must be called upon to ans er some of the questions of quality.

The mention of possible adverse effects of radiation prompts the pleasanter observation that the world of science is not a dismal world. It is a world of hope. What new scientific discoveries remain to be unfolded, discoveries which will ease the burden of our limited resources? Can atomic power release coal for use in developing synthetics? Can we develop a new source of petroleum or equivalents? Can we perfect systems to use lower grade iron ores? Can we control the sea — extracting salts and other valuable minerals, leaving potable water for man and agriculture?

But even if man were to make these discoveries, what effect would that have on population? Will man impede population growth because he fears an economic burden? If so, will a release of some of nature's secrets give man such optimism that he will once again populate the world with frightening speed?

What *has* been the history of man, and his population potential? How did these patterns of growth and decline develop? What factors seem to be related to changes in the birth rate? Can man control the death rate more easily than the birth rate? What countries seem to be on the verge of a population "explosion"? What of the future? What can we learn from the past?

To have a conference on population without an expert in population — the demographer — would be inexcusably foolish. But then, it would be foolish to omit the medical man. It would be just as foolish to ignore the sociologist, the anthropologist, the economist, the geographer, the biologist, the geneticist. All have important things to say. To think clearly on the subject of "population growth" requires us to consider a vast range of ideas, ideas that flow from expert judgment.

What makes an expert? An expert is someone who is truly learned in a particular segment of life. He knows his material as well as it can be known; and if we wish to study our subject of population thoroughly, we will be obliged to obtain and listen to a group of experts.

The testimony of such experts, in brief, is the content of this volume. On a single important subject, each expert, viewing the same data from a different point of view, has given his judgment. Finally, an attempt has been made by qualified commentators to bring these ideas together, to show a common relatedness.

9

The average reader should obtain a worthwhile experience from this volume. If he is not himself an expert in any of these fields, he should nevertheless clearly see how it is that different aspects of a common problem require expert attention. He should also see clearly that each discipline is almost sure to develop a point of view which differs from that of the others in some respects. The problems of life are not simple ones, they are complex. And to solve them, the complex structures must be taken apart and studied, each part calling for an expert judgment.

The reader will also learn something else. He will become aware of limitations of science. For the scientist takes the world apart and studies only a small segment of it; he almost inevitably loses touch with the "reality" that the man in the street occupies and knows. The scientist lives generally, in a timeless world of recurring relations. He enters this phantom world because he excludes the unique. The average person, on the other hand, lives uniquely, in a here-and-now with no variables abstracted.

Most of us will admit that the complex world cannot be apprehended immediately. We concede readily that for purposes of study it must be taken apart. This leads to an important question: who puts it back together? Or, is the world like Humpty Dumpty, who, having been broken by his great fall, can never be put together again?

Earlier I suggested various ways of "integration" — the putting together. Perhaps some are useful only for winning huge prizes on television, or are sterile in their academic approach. Some no doubt are sterile in their disregard of common sense, of underlying principles. To develop a useful common theory takes time — probably several academic generations. But a real start can be made by calling experts together as we have succeeded in doing and getting them to face a common problem. Their technical vocabulary has largely been stripped from them. The sociologist has been forbidden to use differential equations in defining a mathematical model; the anthropologist is not permitted to use the vernacular of the Arunta in discussing human relations; the economist is not allowed to specify his mathematical derivations of supply and demand curves; the geneticist has been warned not to astound us with his Markov chain argument in probability theory; the geographer is denied the use of cartographic vocabulary; the physician is prevented from using the Latin so dear to his *materia medica*. Each has been urged to use, instead of his peculiar jargon, the language of the intelligent American adult. He is likely, to be sure, to lose some precision in using the language system of the everyday world. But on the other hand, if he is able to communicate in such a way that the "non-expert" can approach the problem intelligently, we shall have come a long way.

Let us, then, see what the representatives of the various sciences have to say. We shall be astounded at what we can learn. It is hoped that the scientists will have shared that astonishment.

A Generation of Demographic Change

IT IS desirable to consider first the growth of the total population of the world during the last generation, or roughly the last thirty years, and to compare it with that of the preceding generation. During the last thirty years, the world population has been growing by about 27 million per year. During the preceding thirty years it was growing by about half as large an amount — 14 million per year. The rate of increase has not risen so rapidly, however. During the last thirty years it has been about 12 per thousand per year, compared with about 8 per thousand during the preceding thirty years. In other words there has been roughly a 50 per cent increase in the rate of increase from one generation to the next.

One term we frequently hear used in connection with the world's population growth is "explosion." Is this an appropriate term, or is it an unjustified scare word? During the last generation, as I have said, the number of people has been rising annually about 12 per thousand — or about 1.2 per cent. When businessmen borrow money at an interest rate of 1.2 per cent, they think they are getting it cheaply. And when people who are dependent on investments receive a return of 1.2 per cent per year they feel that it scarcely paid them to save. In the short run the world's recent rate of growth seems rather small.

But when one realizes what such a rate can amount to if it continues over a long time, one's attitude changes radically. When Christ was born the world's inhabitants numbered about 350 million. If that population had grown from 1 A.D. to 1957 at the rate of growth of 1900–1930 — 8 per thousand per year which seems quite small on an annual basis — there would at present be in this world nearly 8 million people for every one person who is now here. If the rate of growth of the last thirty years — about 1.2 per cent which also seems small — had started at the beginning of the Christian Era, we would now have more than 3,000 people per square foot of the world's land area. And if the rate of growth of the last five years — which is only about 1.5 per cent per year — had been in effect we would now have more than one million people per square foot of land. So from the long-time point of view, it seems very appropriate to say that the world is having a population explosion.

Let us look at a crude diagram of the growth of the human species. We are told that mankind first appeared on the earth's surface between five hundred thousand and a million years ago. Let us be conservative, assume that it was five hundred thousand rather than a million years ago, and begin with two people. (Some begin with one person but I prefer starting with one of each sex.) We know very little about man's numbers during most of the five hundred thousand years, merely that from a modern viewpoint the globe had comparatively few inhabitants five thousand years or more before the birth of Christ. At that time, as I have said, the world's population was approximately 350 million. In other words, during nearly all the first 498,000 of the 500,000 years that we are assuming to have passed since the origin of man, the species was increasing at an average rate of about 4 per hundred thousand. Nowadays a city or nation with such a rate would be sure it was standing still rather than growing. And well it might, for if we represent this rate of growth graphically (see Figure 1) the population line for these 498,000 years appears to be practically horizontal. In great contrast is the skyrocketing of people from 350 million to 2,700 million in the last 2,000 years. This appears as an almost vertical line on our diagram, so that the whole picture resembles a right angle.

Before discussing developments in various countries during recent years it may help to reconsider what is referred to as the demographic revolution. In nearly all parts of the world a century or two ago — and in important parts of it today — birth and death rates were at a relatively high level and of approximately the same magnitude; hence little, if any, population increase occurred. Then in some parts the death rate began to go down, fell rapidly for a few decades, and finally began to level off. In a few countries of Europe the birth rates have now also fallen until they approach the death rates on this low level, and again

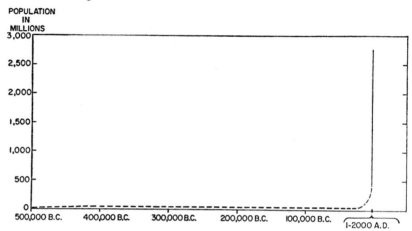

Figure 1. Schematic diagram of the world's population growth

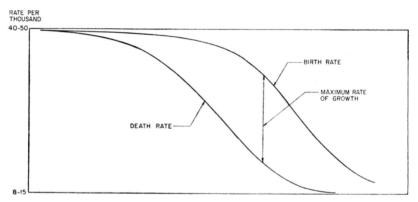

*Figure 2. Model of the demographic revolution, indicating
changes over time*

there is very little population growth. But the death rate has been the
first to fall, only later followed by a decline in the birth rate, and this
is what has brought rapid population increase. A model of these changes
is shown in Figure 2.

Now in general, the countries of the world have been moving along
the path of the demographic revolution during the last generation, and
even during the eight years since the previous symposium on population
was held. This may be seen by comparing birth and death rates for
1955 or 1956 with rates for thirty years earlier. In the United States,

the crude death rate (the number of deaths per thousand population) has declined from 12 to 9. The crude birth rate (about which I'll say more later) is 25 per thousand – the same now as it was a generation ago. (A major decrease in the 1930s was balanced by an increase in the 1940s.) The United States is not behaving quite properly in terms of our schematic diagram, for the rate of natural increase is now about 16 per thousand compared with about 13 a generation earlier. Nevertheless, our country undoubtedly is in the latter part of the demographic revolution, and the changes of the last thirty years probably should be regarded as short-time fluctuations rather than as long-time secular trends.

If we consider the countries to the south of us in Middle and South America, we find a quite different type of change. Thirty years ago, the crude death rate of most of those countries was between 20 and 30 per thousand and falling. We know less about the birth rate because fewer of these countries had fairly complete birth registration, but the indications are that it was high – 40 to 45 per thousand – and close to what is usually thought of as the upper level. The rate of increase for this large region as a whole was in the neighborhood of 15 per thousand. In other words, most of these countries were in an early phase of the demographic revolution.

In the last thirty years there has been a substantial drop in the crude death rate in Middle and South America. In some countries the rate has almost been cut in half and is now down to 10 per thousand. In contrast, the crude birth rate has remained fairly high as a rule – still between 40 and 45 per thousand – although small declines have occurred in some countries, and Chile and Argentina now report rates of 34 and 24, respectively. The larger drop in mortality than in fertility has raised the annual rate of natural increase (population growth) of the region from about 15 per thousand to about 25 per thousand. In other words, most of the American countries to the south of us have been moving toward the middle of the demographic revolution. This region now has a more rapid rate of population growth than any other large area in the world.

Next, let us consider the other extreme – the European countries (excluding the U.S.S.R.) for which we have good information. In this part of the world the crude death rate thirty years ago usually was between 12 and 20 – along the latter part of the death rate line in Figure 2. Since then, it has declined to between 9 and 12 per thousand – nearly as low as it can go. In the same period of time the birth rate has declined from 20–30 per thousand to between 15 and 25 per thousand in most cases. The net result is a small decrease in the rate of population growth, from about 9 to 7 per thousand. Europe is in the second half of the demographic revolution, with some countries much farther along than others.

The situation of Canada, Australia, and New Zealand has been quite like ours, so I won't say anything about them.

We know much less about what has happened in the Asian countries than we do about what has happened in Europe or the Americas. Even now we don't have good vital statistics for a majority of the population of Asia. The best estimates – those of the United Nations – indicate that thirty years ago the crude death rate in most Asian countries was between 30 and 40 per thousand, and that it has declined by now to between 20 and 35. The birth-rate situation resembles that of Middle and South America – the crude rate of most countries being estimated at between 40 and 45 per thousand thirty years ago, and in the neighborhood of 40 per thousand at the present time. In consequence, the rate of natural increase in the Asian region has risen from roughly 10 per thousand to 15 per thousand. Nearly all these countries are in the first part of the demographic revolution.

Japan is an outstanding exception to the general Asian picture. In the last eight years the birth rate has been lowered drastically – from 33 to 19 per thousand. This probably is the most abrupt peacetime drop that has ever occurred in any country during the world's history. Compared with thirty years ago, however, the death rate has gone down nearly as much as the birth rate, and the rate of population growth has only declined from 13 to 11 per thousand. Recently, however, Japan has moved rapidly along the later stages of the demographic revolution.

One of the outstanding cases of rapid population increase is Singapore – another Asian area with very good statistics available. In that city the death rate has been brought down to about 9 per thousand, and the birth rate has remained high (in 1956 it was 48 per thousand), so the rate of natural increase is now 39 per thousand, or 3.9 per cent per year!

It would be interesting to consider some other unusual situations, but instead let me summarize. Broadly speaking, we find that the world's population is now increasing at about 1.5 per cent per year, that the

United States, Canada, Australia, New Zealand, the U.S.S.R., Asia, and Africa are close to the world average, that the rate of 2.5 per cent for Middle and South America is well above the world average, and that Europe's rate of 0.7 per cent is not quite half as large as the world average.

Next, it may be desirable to think about the outlook for future population growth in various areas. Let us begin with the countries in which the demographic revolution has gone furthest, and which have annual growth rates of less than 1 per cent. Nearly all these countries are in Europe. In most of them the crude death rate is about as low as it can go. In fact, in some cases this rate is likely to rise as the proportion of middle-aged and older people in the population increases. Birth rates also are relatively low, in most cases because a large majority of married couples wish to have small families and are successful in their efforts to prevent unwanted pregnancies. In these countries the rate of growth during coming years will depend chiefly on the average number of children that married couples want to have. This number may go up in some countries if economic conditions improve, if programs to favor larger families are adopted, or if changes in value systems place more emphasis on children as compared with economic goods. On the other hand, changes in the opposite direction may occur, and tend to reduce the average number of children wanted. Predicting the future trends of such conditions is highly speculative. Moreover, little is known about the relative importance of the numerous factors influencing the decisions of couples on having another child; hence we lack an adequate basis for evaluating the extent to which a known change in a given factor — for example, in economic conditions — would raise or lower the number of children wanted. We can be fairly sure, however, that actual family size will move closer to desired family size as married couples become better informed about contraceptive methods, and as more effective and acceptable methods are developed. On the whole, therefore, I expect these countries will continue to move along the path of the demographic revolution, and to have slowly decreasing rates of growth. In the short run, if important fluctuations in economic conditions occur, there undoubtedly will be important short-run changes in fertility and population increase.

Among the countries with medium growth rates — that is, between 1 and 2 per cent per year — we find such a wide variation in conditions that generalization is impossible. I mentioned Africa as growing on the whole at about the world rate of 1.5 per cent per year. In some parts of Africa it is practically certain that death rates will be lowered and that the number of people will rise more rapidly. If out of each thousand babies that are born in a year, four hundred die before their first birthday, as has been the case in some Egyptian villages in recent years, there is plenty of opportunity for reducing death rates substantially! In contrast, other countries or groups of people — for example, the French in North Africa and the white population of the Union of South Africa — are in the latter part of the demographic revolution, and their rate of growth is more likely to taper off than to go up.

There are others who can speak better than I about what is likely to happen in the U.S.S.R., another country with a medium rate of growth. I expect some reduction to occur, for I think that more and more of the Russian people will come to realize that having too many children tends to depress the level of living of a family.

Eastern Asia as a whole has a rate of growth only slightly above the world average. In China I think the likelihood is that population growth will become somewhat more rapid as death rates are reduced through public health measures. Recently, however, some of the Communist leaders have been pointing out the need for family limitation so that the lower death rates which are desired (and anticipated) will not mean large additions to the 600,000,000 people now present whose living levels are to be raised. It is possible that these discussions will lead to a program enforced with the power that a Communist regime can use, which will lower birth rates more quickly than death rates and slow down population growth rather than speed it up. If this happens, China will go through the demographic revolution much more rapidly than the United States and the countries of northwestern Europe.

Southeastern Asia has a rate of growth of about 1.8 per cent per year according to the United Nations' estimates. It is likely to go even higher for a time, for the reasons first mentioned in discussing China.

South central Asia, of which India has a major part of the population, is now thought to be growing at about 1.2 per cent per year. There too, I think some increase in the rate of growth is to be expected, for public health programs and other changes are likely to reduce death rates. But here again a major uncertainty is what will happen to the birth rate. Will the government of India be successful with the program it is planning to spread information about a relatively simple and fairly effective method of contraception among married couples throughout rural India? Ten million rupees is budgeted for that project over a five-year period as a part of the second five-year plan. That is only a little more than 2 million dollars, which to us is not a large amount, and which certainly doesn't seem large on a per capita basis for India. But one must remember that in terms of human time a rupee will buy as much in India as a dollar here, so from the standpoint of purchasing power 10 million rupees is not too far from 10 million dollars.

So far as I know India is the first country to make a large-scale attempt to reduce birth rates by spreading information about contraception. In this respect it is a great pioneer for the heavily populated and underdeveloped countries. Many people are quite pessimistic about what can be done, while others are moderately optimistic. It is possible that the program will have little impact, but it is also possible that it will be surprisingly effective and that a substantial beginning will be made in the next five years in lowering the birth rate in India and speeding it toward the end of the demographic revolution. The results will be awaited with great interest.

Reserving for the end of my paper a more detailed discussion of the United States, which is also among the countries with a medium rate of growth, I would like now to pass on to the last of the three groups I mentioned.

The rapidly growing areas, with a rate of more than 2 per cent per year, consist mainly of Middle and South America, the Philippines, and parts of Oceania. For Middle and South America the outlook for the next few years probably is for little reduction in the rate of growth. While fertility probably will decline, there is a good chance that this change will be balanced by a further decline in mortality. In other words, this region as a whole probably has not reached the midpoint of the demographic revolution. Argentina is an important exception. Its rate of natural increase already has been lowered to 16 per thousand, and the downward trend is likely to continue.

I have been talking so far about birth rates, death rates, and rates of natural increase, and have not said anything about international migration because during most of the world's history it has had only a very slight effect on the rate of growth of the total population. In theory,

19

international migration should take people from areas where there is overcrowding to areas with greater economic opportunity, which should speed up the world's growth. In practice, large-scale movements concentrated in a few decades have occurred only intermittently. European migration to the Americas was one of the major movements, but even here the crucial factor was not the number of people who crossed the ocean. Vastly more important was the fact that the comparatively few who came brought a different civilization which replaced the indigenous hunting and fishing economy and enabled a given amount of land to support far more people than it had supported previously.

Within the last generation, one of the largest movements of people across national boundaries has been the migration of Moslems from India to Pakistan and of Hindus from Pakistan into India. It is estimated that about 10 million Hindus went to India, and a substantially smaller number of Moslems went to Pakistan. But even this huge interchange has had relatively little effect on the total number of people in each country, and no measurable effect on the growth rate of the world. If we define international migration more strictly, and rule out movements like the foregoing on the ground that they reflect changes in national boundaries following a war or other unusual event, we find that during the last thirty years the United States has received more immigrants than any other country. But the net inward movement has amounted to only about 3 million people, or an average of about one hundred thousand a year, which is of minor importance compared with our rate of natural increase from the excess of births over deaths.

Because we are Americans we are especially interested in what has been happening to population growth in the United States and what is likely to happen in the future. Our population on January 1, 1957, was very close to 170 million. For the last ten years we have been growing by about 2.7 million per year. During the last thirty years, and the preceding thirty years as well, the increase was close to 50 million people, or 1.7 million per year. Many persons have read so much about the postwar jump in the birth rate and know of so many families in which young married couples are having more children than their parents that they think the United States has been growing recently at a record-breaking rate as well as by record-breaking numbers. This is incorrect. In the last ten years our annual rate of growth has averaged about 1.5 per cent. Although this is well above the rate of about 1.2 per cent for the last thirty years as a whole, it is well below the rate of 1.7 per cent for the preceding thirty years and barely half the rate which prevailed most of the time from 1700 to 1860.

It is interesting to consider different portions of the last thirty years, because of the great contrasts that are found – for example, the depression decade of the 1930s and the decade of prosperity since World War II. If we compare these two periods we find for one thing that there were about 22 million births in the former and about 38 million in the latter. This is a jump of more than 70 per cent, which is most unusual. People are right in speaking of the great upsurge in numbers of births and in the birth rate since the war – the baby boom, as it is sometimes called. But are they right in saying (as so many do) that the chief cause is larger families? Let us see, for that will help us to understand what is likely to happen in the next decade or two.

First, however, let us rule out about 25 per cent of the increase in the number of births, because it merely reflects the fact that the population was larger in the last ten years than it was during the 1930s. We can do this by considering the crude birth rate instead of the number of births. The crude birth rate averaged 17.3 per thousand during the 1930s and 24.6 per thousand during 1947 to 1956. This rise of 42 per cent is much smaller than that of 70 per cent for the number of births; nevertheless, it too is unusual in world history.

When I ask people what they think has been the most important factor in raising our birth rate so greatly, the answer almost always is "Families are getting larger." There has been a change in that direction, but if we measure family size on the basis of the average number of births per couple with children, we find that the increase in this number has contributed only about one-sixth of the birth-rate rise we are discussing.

Other explanations are that more women are marrying, and that those who do so are marrying younger. The former is not important, because for many decades about 90 per cent of American women married before reaching the end of the childbearing period, and the rise so far has not reached 94 per cent. Even if it were to continue to 100 per cent (which is most unlikely) the relative change would not be large. Much more important as a cause of the postwar baby boom is the younger marriage of more women. For example, at the end of the 1930s approximately 53 per cent of the women aged 20–24 (and born in 1916–

20) had already married, but in 1955 the proportion married by ages 20–24 had risen to 71 per cent for women born in 1931–35. This is a large increase. Together with the small decrease in the number of old maids it has contributed about 40 per cent of the rise in the crude birth rate from the 1930s to 1947–56.

The third (and last) change I shall mention is the tendency for more married women to have at least one child and to start childbearing sooner after marriage. In 1940 approximately 33 per cent of the women aged 20–24 who had married had not yet borne a child. By 1955 the corresponding proportion had fallen to 25 per cent. Similarly, among women aged 25–29 who had ever been married those without children decreased from 26 per cent of the total in 1940 to 13 per cent in 1955. Such changes have contributed more than 40 per cent of the rise in the crude birth rate from the 1930s to the postwar decade.

You may say that if fewer wives are childless and more have one child, this helps just as much to increase average family size as having three children instead of two. This is correct. I have mentioned the two types of change separately in order to emphasize the fact that the increase in family size that is under way results chiefly from some couples having one or two children instead of none, some having two or three instead of one, and some having three or four instead of two. This is far from a return to the large-family pattern of a century ago.

If we put all types of increase together we still find that less than half of the rise in annual fertility from the depression low to the postwar high is attributable to more children per married couple, and more than half to the fact that women are marrying younger and having their first child at a younger age. The latter circumstance has moved to the past ten years some millions of births that would have occurred during the next ten years if the former pattern of age at marriage and the first confinement had continued.

Most of us who are concerned with population problems professionally tend to overestimate the increase in size of family that has been going on, because it has been larger on the whole in the upper educational and income groups — the groups that we are likely to know about firsthand — than in the rest of the population. We tend to judge the situation as a whole by what happens to the people we know about. We have fewer friends in the lower educational and income classes where average size of family has still been going down.

22

What is the outlook for the future? Will the high annual birth rate of recent years be maintained? The tendency for women to marry and start childbearing younger is a temporary factor. As long as the age at marriage is dropping, the birth rate will be supported at a relatively high level by that influence. But once the age at marriage stops going down, the birth rate does not remain on that plateau but declines to a lower level. A big question, then, is how much longer will the age of women flocking to the altar and to the maternity ward a year or two later decline? I think age of marriage may continue to decline, but there certainly is a limit below which it is not likely to go. It is one thing for the median age — the age by which half the women who will marry have done so — to decrease from between 21 and 22 among the women born during 1916–20 to less than 20 among those born during 1926–30. But it will be another thing if the decline continues to 18 or younger. Similarly, the shortening of the average interval between marriage and the first baby is a temporary factor, which raises the annual birth rate while it is going on, but lets it fall once the new shorter interval is established. Here again it is one thing for the average length of the first interval to decline from about 34 months for women born during 1916–20 to 24 months for those born during 1926–30, and another thing for it to decline to 14 months. There is no chance of its going as low as nine months in our population!

It is evident from what I have said that only a substantial increase in the average number of children per family can keep our birth rate from declining. Such an increase would not be temporary in its influence (as is the case with younger marriage and earlier childbearing) but would help to maintain a higher birth rate even though family size should become stable at a level only somewhat above that of the recent past. But what is likely to happen to family size in coming years? The best information now available comes from a study of a representative sample — what the statistician calls a "probability sample" — of the white married couples in the United States with the wife between the ages of 18 and 39. This information was collected about two years ago and is now in the process of being analyzed. It shows that some increase in the size of completed families is almost certain to occur, but not as large an increase as is commonly thought. For example, among the women who were at the end of the childbearing period at the beginning of 1955 (i.e., who were then 45–49 years old) there had been an average of about 2.40 births per woman who had married. This lifetime birth rate is certain to go higher in coming years, for in 1955 among the women aged 35–39 who had ever been married there had already been about 2.50 births per woman and another .15 to .45 were expected. Among still younger women — aged 25–29 — the rate by 1955 had been lower, but these women confidently expected to have at least 2.7 births each and possibly as many as 3.3, and gave 3.0 as a most probable figure. An increase from 2.4 to 3.0 children per ever-married woman would represent a substantial reversal of the long-time downward trend of family size in the United States. It would regain only a fraction of the past decrease, however, for the average married woman aged 45 in 1910 had borne 4.3 children, and half a century earlier the average probably was about 6.0. In consequence, I think it is quite likely that the crude birth rate and the rate of population growth will start down within five or ten years, and certainly will do so within fifteen years.

The speed and size of the decline will depend in part on economic conditions, but the desires of our millions of married couples will play a more important role. The birth rate in the United States, as in several other countries, is largely under voluntary control. Among the white married couples with the wife between the ages of 18 and 39 in the study to which I referred earlier, about 70 per cent had tried to space their children or to limit their number. Another 9 per cent, mostly young married couples, had not done so as yet, but expected to do so in the future. So 79 per cent can be called family planners, at least in intent. The remaining 21 per cent include 5 per cent that were definitely sterile and not interested in contraception. Another 9 per cent were probably sterile or had had so much difficulty in conceiving that they felt little need for control measures. This leaves only about 6 per cent that conceived easily and did not expect to use some method of birth control to space children or limit their number. If we consider only the fecund couples — those that conceived easily — we find that about 83 per cent had already used contraception, another 7 per cent expected to do so, and only about 10 per cent said they would not try any type of family planning. The latter group contains a substantial number of younger couples who have not been married long, some of whom are likely to change their minds after they have three, four, or five children. The experience of the older couples shows numerous

24

additions to the ranks of the family planners after the birth of an additional baby. In fact, having an additional child seems to be a strong incentive to the practice of contraception.

If we look at the relation between the family size desired by the fecund couples and the actual number of their children, we find that only about 14 per cent said they had more children than they wanted, and that in most cases the excess was only one. As would be expected, few of the younger couples had more than they wanted, though some of them no doubt will as time passes. But even among the fecund couples with the wife aged 35–39, only 22 per cent are in the excess fertility group. (Among those who had not tried control measures the percentage is 40.) It seems fair to say that a rather high degree of success in controlling fertility has been achieved.

It is clear that population growth in the United States during the next few decades will depend primarily on marriage patterns and on the attitudes of married couples regarding family size. These can change quite rapidly, as we have seen by comparing the last ten years with the 1930s. The United States has been unusually prosperous since World War II. If prosperity is maintained we probably shall have for a time a continued trend toward somewhat larger families, but shall soon see the stabilization of marriage and the first confinement at ages only a little below those now customary. The result will be a decrease in the birth rate and the rate of population growth to somewhat lower levels. If there is a recession we undoubtedly shall see sharper decreases in both these rates. And if we have a major depression like the 1930s — which does not seem likely but might possibly happen — the birth rate probably will go down with startling rapidity, because the tendencies to marry younger, to have the first child come sooner, and to want larger families will all be reversed. This is an extreme that we should not overlook entirely even though it now appears quite improbable.

In contrast to the outlook for some slowing down of population growth in the United States, the global outlook is for more rapid growth. The underdeveloped countries with a large proportion of the world's population can reduce death rates rapidly by developing good public health programs, and speed up population growth accordingly. The crucial question is what will happen to their birth rates. Will countries like India and China be as successful in reducing fertility as in reducing mortality? If so, their demographic revolution will be over

25

in much less time than in most of the developed countries, and the explosive growth of the world's population shown in Figure 1 will be brought under control, perhaps within a century. If not, man's ingenuity faces the staggering task of providing for his rapidly growing numbers, and doing so not as in the past but on the rising level of living that is so widely wanted.

∞

Minimum Subsistence

WHILE "minimum subsistence" is an important subject, and appropriate for a symposium on population, I hope I shall make it clear that "minimum" is only a qualitative descriptive term and that there is an unbroken continuum from subsistence at a level that produces death from starvation in a month or two to the super-luxus consumption level that also produces death but requires years to do so.

What we really want to know, I think, is what are the relationships between the level of subsistence and such matters as health, strength, reproduction, economic productivity, and political stability. These questions may be incapable of precise analysis and answers because we must reckon with the powerful forces of human motivation and attitudes, forces that are relatively independent variables. However, we can certainly speak about general tendencies.

For the past three hundred years the world population has been increasing steadily and the problem of food for the future world population has been debated for nearly two hundred years. Beginning with Malthus, in 1798, or even with Süssmilch before him, the first concern about population increase has been with the elementary problem of feeding an ever-increasing world family. Repeatedly it has been pointed out that a large proportion of the world's inhabitants are chronically hungry and near to starvation. What then will happen if every year we add more millions of people who must be fed?

Actually, there is every reason to believe that, on the average, the 2,700 million people today are further removed from starvation than the 1,300 million of a little over a century ago. So may we not cease worrying and trust that the future needs will somehow be met as they have been in the past?

We could, but I think we must all agree that no satisfactory adjustment of food supplies to food needs will come about *automatically*. At the very least we must inquire into the technical possibilities and problems, we must estimate the future needs, roughly at least, and examine the resources available to meet them. This means that we, and by "we" I mean the United States and Canada, must consider production and distribution of food on a global basis. For no matter what may be the food potential of the United States and Canada to meet our own rapidly expanding needs, we cannot forget the primary place of food in the political problems of the world. There is no greater force behind political strife than hunger or the threat of hunger.

FOOD NEEDS

Calories. The most immediate and elementary food need is the need for food energy, that is, for calories. How many calories do we need? As chairman of the Calories Committee of the United Nations' Food and Agriculture Organization since its formation in 1949, I have had long experience with the difficulties of estimating this basic food requirement for populations. At our most recent meeting, it was evident that although such estimation is still difficult for individuals it is possible to develop satisfactory standards for populations.

The Calories Committee has consistently agreed that all food planning about calorie requirements should be based on the needs of fully healthy individuals pursuing an active and productive life. With this guide, we have recommended a procedure for estimating the needs of populations. Briefly, allowance is made according to age, body size, sex, climate, and degree of activity. We have agreed that race is not influential and that for most populations the distribution of activities between population segments and throughout the year tends to result in considerable uniformity of whole populations in their calorie needs for physical activity. Hence, for most purposes we arrive at suitable calorie allowances for a population simply from a knowledge of the average temperature to which it is exposed, the average body size of adults, and the population structure in terms of age and sex.

Of two populations with the same age structure and average body size, one living at a mean annual temperature of 25° C. will need about

7 per cent fewer calories than an equivalent population living at a mean temperature of 10° C. The influence of body size is such that, other things being equal, a population in which the average male adult weighs 65 kilograms will need about 15 per cent more calories than a population in which the average man weighs only 50 kilograms. At the same body weight, adult females require about 20 per cent fewer calories than adult males of the same age. We estimate that among adults of the same size, the calorie need declines about 5 per cent for each decade after age thirty. Finally, the estimation of the calorie needs of infants and children has been provided for in a similar physiological analysis which is too complex to discuss here.

This system has been widely used by the specialized agencies of the United Nations and by many of the member countries. Very satisfactory agreement between theory and observation has been reported. Some minor discrepancies, less than 10 per cent for any population reporting, were resolved by modification of our 1950 recommendations and at the committee's 1956 session it appeared that the errors in our estimates are less than 5 per cent for every country reporting.

These calorie requirement estimates are at the physiological level — that is, they refer to food actually eaten. Food production must be considerably greater, of course, to allow for waste. Between the wholesaler and the consumer, waste may range up to 30 per cent or more but a fair average may be something like 20 to 25 per cent. Waste is high in the United States because we produce and buy more than we need and we do not bother to save it. Waste may be equally high in many poor countries because of their lack of facilities to protect food from insects and spoilage.

We can, then, estimate with reasonable accuracy the food calories we need to eat, and when we translate this into terms of food production requirements the result is probably within plus or minus 10 per cent of the true value. Such estimates, of course, apply to the world as it is today, with the present manner of living and working. But what of the future? What may be expected if mechanization continues to displace manual labor? And what will be the result when heating and insulation lessen the need for food calories to keep us warm?

Effects of Technological Advance. The possibilities in technological advance can be estimated with no great error. In the first place, the common belief that there are enormous differences between the energy needs of manual laborers and sedentary and mechanized workers is er-roneous. The calorie expenditures on the job differ a good deal to be sure, especially when we measure only the peak activity of the manual worker, but the weekly or, better, yearly averages are not so different. The lumberjack at the peak of his winter labor in cold weather may reach a bit over 5,000 calories per day and this is about the top of human energy expenditure. But his average for the season is probably not much over 4,000 calories and his average for the year is more like 3,600 calories. His mechanized counterpart, say the truck driver, will average between 3,000 and 3,500 calories.

We cannot avoid a little technical analysis if we are to understand calorie needs. An example, given in Table 1, may be helpful. Let us

Table 1. Calories Expended per Week by a Logger, a Trucker, and a Professor *

Item	Logger	Trucker	Professor
Basal metabolism	10,080	10,080	10,080
Extra energy cost of job	11,520	4,800	2,400
All other activity	3,840	4,320	4,320
Total	25,440	19,200	16,800
Specific dynamic action	2,544	1,920	1,680
Grand total calories for the week..........	27,984	21,120	18,480

* The logger works 48 hours, the others 40; all sleep 56 hours.

consider a lumberjack, a truck driver, and a university professor, all the same size and age. And let us be old-fashioned about the lumber-jack; he works 48 hours a week while the other men work only 40. They all use the same calories for basal metabolism, that is, the energy needed to keep the body alive but "idling," so to speak. This may aver-age 60 calories per hour for the men we are considering. During the week they spend less than one fourth of their time at their jobs. The lumberjack burns up energy on his job at five times the basal rate, the truck driver works at about three times the basal rate, and the pro-fessor at about two times the basal rate. Off the job they all average two times the basal rate per hour.

The daily averages are 3,998, 3,017, and 2,670 calories, including an allowance of 10 per cent for specific dynamic action, the cost of digest-ing and metabolizing food. This last is directly proportional to the amount of food eaten. In percentage terms the truck driver needs about

75 per cent of the logger's calories, the professor about 67 per cent. But if we had considered only the energy cost of the different jobs we would have rated the trucker at 42 and the professor at 21 per cent of the logger's calories.

From such calculations we can estimate that the ultimate possible reduction in calorie needs per person resulting from complete mechanization and all labor-saving devices would be only about 20 per cent for the world as a whole and perhaps 10 per cent for the United States.

The effect of protection from cold can be estimated also and it turns out to be a saving of less than 10 per cent in food calories for the coldest countries and a world average of perhaps 3 per cent. In sum, then, we can confidently predict that the world average of calorie requirements per person will never be much less than 80 per cent of what they are today.

Specific Nutrients. So far I have discussed only calories; certainly it must be constantly borne in mind that the needs for proteins, vitamins, and minerals are not automatically covered merely by providing enough calories. The possibility of deficiency in specific nutrients, especially in vitamins, has been greatly increased in modern times by the development of food processing.

Refining processes yield food products that are attractive to the eye, acceptable to the taste, and remarkably resistant to spoilage. The latter virtue has enormous commercial advantage but often enough is associated with the removal or destruction of vitamins, and sometimes minerals, to an extent that makes nutritionists sympathize with raw-food faddists. We can, of course, buy the minerals and some of the vitamins at the drugstore but this is an expensive and inadequate way of correcting the damage.

However, in terms of future population needs for nutrients, I venture to predict that neither vitamin nor mineral shortages will be critical. Chemical technology, including the use of microbiology, can surely provide in the future almost unlimited amounts of these accessory food factors. Food technologists, too, are paying more attention to nutrient quality and if their methods deprive our foods of their natural vitamins they are increasingly ready and able to put at least some of them back into their products before they ask us to eat them.

Proteins present more difficult problems but here again I am optimistic about the basic nutritional future. I do not mean that we can foresee a plenty of the so-called protein foods — meats, poultry, and dairy products. Meats will continue to be our most expensive nutriment and I think it impossible that the populations of the poorer countries will ever have much more meat per capita than they do now. But our protein needs can be met with little or no meat, if need be. It is now recognized that we require certain amino acids and the total of the correct amino acids adds up to the equivalent of relatively little animal protein. Moreover, there is no reason to doubt that, if the need arises, chemical industry could synthesize amino acids in far larger quantity than any foreseeable expansion of animal husbandry could.

In India at the present time there is serious discussion as to whether that country's apparently desperate food future may not be relieved better by great development of chemical food technology rather than by pursuing the hopeless goal of expanding agricultural production of all foods. The idea, as developed by my one-time colleague Dr. G. Sankaran, would be to concentrate farming on the most productive calorie staples and to synthesize the vitamins and proteins needed to make a good diet.

But to return to the subject of minimum subsistence. When the calorie supply of a people is reduced, shortages of proteins and vitamins need not be serious problems. Nowhere in Europe were there real difficulties with protein or vitamin deficiencies during World War II, though in some areas calorie shortages were severe. The reason for this is that the very effort to make the fullest use of food resources also tends to improve the utilization of proteins and vitamins. Flour is not extracted to 70 per cent, thereby sacrificing most of the vitamins and a good deal of protein. Sugar and refined fats and oils usually disappear and are replaced by potatoes, vegetables, and local fruits and berries, which makes for a net increase in both proteins and vitamins.

The situation is different in some other parts of the world, of course, because of the habitual use of foods that are unusually poor in everything but carbohydrate. But even in those regions much of the vitamin deficiency could be easily prevented by adopting other methods of preparing the foods. Beriberi, the worst of the nutritional disorders in southeast Asia, could be eliminated merely by changing methods of milling and cooking rice.

In connection with this question of the future population needs for nutrients other than calories, the only real danger is that overconcentration on calorie production could lead to relative overproduction of high-calorie-yield crops such as cassava, sweet potatoes, and sugar cane. Such food items, and foolish insistence on various food-refining methods, are the main reasons for the endemic malnutrition of many tropical and subtropical regions.

In the United States and in many of the more prosperous regions of the world we are creating a somewhat analogous set of nutritional problems by the increasing use of refined oils and fats. These are highly concentrated sources of calories but they carry almost no other nutrients. When, as at present, we get more than 40 per cent of our calories from fats, we are displacing other nutrients of wider nutritional value from our diets. Even potatoes and flour are far better nutritionally than fats. They would be excellent foods if we would prepare them a little more sensibly.

Further, there is now much reason to believe that the excessive use of fats in our diets is involved in the most pressing American health problem of today — coronary heart disease. I cannot here discuss this large and important subject in the study of which I am deeply engaged. But I think it may be amusing and perhaps thought-provoking to quote from that great medical journal the *Lancet*. This is from the issue of May 5, 1956:

Once upon a time there was a very poor country, where nobody had enough to eat and the average expectation of life was 24 years. There was also a very rich country, where everybody had plenty to eat and the average expectation of life was 64 years. In the very rich country people used to save up milk and butter and cream and eggs and send them to the very poor country, where they were distributed, especially to the children, who would otherwise have had none. In this way the expectation of life in the very poor country was raised from 24 to 27 years. Meanwhile the expectation of life in the very rich country was rising too, and went up from 64 to 67 years, and everyone who didn't die of cancer of the lung from smoking too many cigarettes died of coronary thrombosis. Then someone discovered that coronary thrombosis was due to eating and drinking too much milk and butter and cream and eggs. So people stopped eating and drinking milk and butter and cream and eggs in the very rich country, and sent it all to the very poor country so that the expectation of life in the very poor country might be raised high enough for them to start dying of coronary thrombosis so that they, too, could stop eating and drinking milk and butter and cream and eggs.

So much for food needs — the needs of human populations for calories and specific nutrients. Let us now turn to the question of what happens when the per capita food supply is reduced.

UNDERNUTRITION

What happens when food requirements are not met? What do people do and what happens to them? First, we shall be able to inquire into the results of a newly developed food shortage because, unfortunately, we have been able to observe this situation at all levels of shortage during and after World War II.

Food prices rise unless there is very effective price control. If the food shortage is great no control scheme can prevent an increase in the real cost of food. When you are hungry you will barter your goods and your labor as well as your money to get more food; the law of supply and demand operates.

Food hoarding and efforts to reduce food waste are obvious first results of a general shortage. Very quickly there is a shift from the more expensive to the more abundant foods and agricultural production changes to concentrate on food items of quick and large yield. People eat less meat and butter and more bread and potatoes and cabbage. The change in the character of the diet is greater than the change in actual calories eaten but even so calorie intake falls and people lose weight.

Within limits this may not be so bad as judged by the world experience in World War II. When the food shortage is such that the calorie consumption is reduced by something like 10 per cent in the countries of western and northern Europe, there is no indication of a bad effect on health. On the contrary, the general mortality rate falls, notably in deaths from heart disease, and there is a reduction in diabetes and dental caries. And there is little or no lessening in work capacity. People grumble and a few unfortunates really suffer but on the whole we and the British and the Swedes and so on can do very well on 90 per cent of what we now eat.

This is the situation in countries where nutrition was adequate before the food shortage and where distribution is fairly equitable. In countries where undernutrition is chronic, a new food shortage causing a reduction of 10 per cent in calorie intake has very different consequences. In such countries there is always a sizable proportion of the population whose food intake is already less than enough to allow full activity and their productivity is low accordingly. Reduce their food another 10 per cent and some of them cannot work at all. They either starve to death or become a charge on the rest of the community.

With greater food shortages the results are increasingly unfavorable, of course. But even a reduction as great as 25 or 30 per cent from our full "requirement" level need not be completely catastrophic. If the reduced food supplies are equitably distributed, subsistence at the 70 per cent level produces marked losses in body weight and some reduction in work capacity, especially in manual labor, but life can go on. At this subsistence level people do not continue to lose more and more weight and then die of starvation when their bodily fat is exhausted.

The reason is that we can adapt to widely different levels of food intake. Even if we continue at the same job and do not greatly change our work level, after some months on a reduced food intake we strike a new energy balance. We, or rather our bodies, learn how to live with a smaller calorie expenditure. There are three main elements in this.

In the first place, as we lose weight our basal metabolism decreases. The "saving" from this may amount to 25 per cent of our former basal metabolism. Second, we automatically reduce the number, speed, and violence of our muscular movements so that our energy expenditure on the job, and even more so in voluntary activities off the job, is much decreased. Third, since the specific dynamic action remains at 10 per cent of the actual food eaten, there is an appreciable saving there too. And the net result is that after a time there is no further loss of weight and calorie balance is achieved on an intake only 70 per cent of the pre-food-shortage level.

But we now have a population in which some members who fail to get their share will actually die of starvation and the population as a whole is physically weak and is apathetic and irritable by turns. Most important, social consciousness evaporates, petty thievery and dishonesty are rampant, and political ideals and cohesion give way to demagoguery, corruption, and dictatorship. This unhappy picture characterizes a protracted famine and equally well describes the chronic situation among large sectors of the population in the poorest parts of the world today.

In natural situations, severe food shortages are almost invariably associated with other shortages — soap, housing, clothing, fuel, medical supplies — and it is not surprising that the health picture of the population usually deteriorates. Until recent decades, famine has always been associated with pestilence and it was customary to blame undernutrition alone for the result. But the experience of World War II showed that this is not necessarily the case. If the medical services are well maintained, epidemics do not break out among ill-fed and even starving people. It is now possible for people to starve wholesale without the complications of cholera and typhus.

Tuberculosis may be a special case, however. The epidemic character of tuberculosis in war prison camps is largely explained by overcrowding and bad sanitation but semistarvation may also render people more susceptible to this infection. And once the disease is contracted, the resistance to it of the underfed body is very low.

Modern studies on mass undernutrition and starvation show that the greatest sufferers are not necessarily the women and children. In terms of mortality and morbidity they prove to do better, on the average, than the adult men. The highest mortality is almost always among the old men. The old women do badly too but they seem to have more endurance and better powers of physiological adaptation. Among the children, the young infants show high mortality, mainly because their special food needs are often hard to meet and they cannot tolerate the coarse foods to which the community may be driven.

The rate of growth of children is slowed by undernutrition. Not only do they become thin and fail to gain weight as they should; linear growth is also retarded. Such "stunting" is not permanent, however, at least if the period of real undernutrition is limited to three or four years. If they are later re-fed, they catch up, as was clearly shown by follow-up studies on children who were seriously underfed in Central Europe during World War I. Ten years later they were fully up to the expectations for both height and weight of youngsters who had always been well fed.

RESIDUES OF UNDERNUTRITION

What I have said about the growth of children anticipates some of my comments on the residues of a period of undernutrition. Any such experience — a prolonged period when it is simply not possible to get enough to eat and when hunger is never stilled — must leave psychological residues. This is a great emotional experience and the person cannot escape some consequences. The consequences are not necessarily bad,

36

but the person's outlook, philosophy, and attitudes will certainly be altered.

The physical and physiological residues have been inadequately studied. If only calorie undernutrition is involved, with no marked deficiencies of vitamins and minerals, it appears that full or nearly full physical recovery may be expected, even after extreme semistarvation. This seems to be the case, at least, with children and young adults. Whether older persons recover fully is not clear. But if the food shortage involves severe vitamin deficiencies, there may be permanent damage, especially to the nervous system and to the special senses. Cases of this kind came out of the prison and concentration camps of the Far East at the end of World War II. Nothing like this problem emerged from the prisons and camps of Europe where starvation was often worse than in the Orient.

REPRODUCTION

In a conference on population the question of the effect of nutrition on human reproduction is obviously important. However, the facts available for discussion are not numerous and in human populations the influence of nutrition is seldom if ever operating as a single variable.

Extreme undernutrition soon extinguishes the reproductive urge or ability or both. By "soon" I mean a matter of some months and by "extreme" I mean where the caloric intake falls to 50 per cent or less of the requirements. This effect is interesting but has only limited practical relevance because it is associated with a degree of underfeeding that also destroys work capacity and is clearly not compatible with the continued life of a society.

More moderate degrees of undernutrition produce little or no hindrance to reproduction, as witnesss the fact that the worst population pressures are apt to be in areas where there is chronic hunger. The latter fact has been seized on by Dr. Josué de Castro of Brazil in developing a challenging thesis in his book *The Geography of Hunger*.

The crucial point of his argument is that "overpopulation does not cause starvation in various parts of the world, but that starvation is the cause of overpopulation." De Castro makes much of the fact, as he states it, that "the groups with the highest fertility are those who have the lowest percentage of complete animal proteins in their diets." Like many other alleged "facts" in de Castro's book, this is open to serious question and other explanations are ready at hand for such truth as there is in his sweeping statements.

De Castro has two main theories to support his idea that a high rate of population increase is attributable to malnutrition. First, he says, "The psychological effect of chronic hunger is to make sex important enough to compensate emotionally for the shrunken nutritional appetite. . . . When chronic hunger, then, particularly hunger for proteins and certain vitamins produces chronic lack of appetite and loss of interest in food, the sexual instinct becomes dominant."

This statement is replete with error. I can assure you that chronic undernutrition or chronic subsistence on very small amounts of animal proteins does not produce a "shrunken appetite" or "loss of interest in food." And I have seen no relationship between the sexual instinct and the level of nutrition except, as I have said, in real starvation where the sex drive disappears. In some primitive societies and in some cultures different from our own where the nutritional level is low, sex and the sex act are more openly cultivated. But to the best of my knowledge there is no reason to believe that there is any consistent pattern in the frequency of sexual relations that follows the nutritional pattern anywhere. It is fantastic to suggest that the birth rate in France is low because the French seldom indulge in intercourse or that it is high in India for the opposite reason. For the world as a whole I think we must all agree that the relationship between the number of opportunities for conception and the number of births is very low indeed.

The second theory of de Castro is that sterility is produced by diets rich in proteins. In proof he cited some old experiments of Slonaker with rats in which a high percentage of the rats were sterile on diets providing 18 or 22 per cent of their calories from proteins. So, de Castro says, if we just make sure the Indians get more protein in their diet, they will stop making so many babies. But thousands of rat experiments have been made since Slonaker's time and I believe they offer no confirmation of this theory at all. More important, de Castro simply did not bother to look into the available figures on birth rates and diets the world 'round.

I can cite three countries where I have recently conducted personal researches on diets and health—Italy, Japan, and the United States. The birth rate in Italy is low, in the United States high, and in Japan was higher still until very recently. The percentage of calories supplied by proteins in the diets is almost identical in the three countries. The percentage of calories from proteins from animal sources is high in the United States, low in Italy, and very low in Japan.

All in all, Dr. de Castro's thesis is provocative but simply not defensible. And the vital point about population increases everywhere is that they are the result not of increasing birth rates but of decreasing death rates.

A LOOK TO THE FUTURE

Now just a word in conclusion. Agricultural experts can tell us how much more land can be used for food production and how much more food can be produced per acre using methods already at hand. Let me speculate about the food saving we could achieve by reducing waste, by reducing overeating, and by decreasing energy expenditure through mechanization and through avoiding the use of food calories to keep warm. Worldwide mechanization might save 10 per cent of the world's food calories. Curbing overeating the world over would probably save 1 or 2 per cent of all our calories, and better heating and insulation might have an equal effect. Finally, I believe that a 10 per cent saving by reducing waste and spoilage is entirely possible to achieve. The sum total is around 23 per cent.

This means that if the world population today is 2,700 million, then we could feed another 600 million people without increasing our food production at all — if, and this is a big if of course, we use other sources of energy besides food calories to do most of the hard physical work of the world and to keep us warm, if we can successfully combat obesity and overeating, and if we cut our present food waste and spoilage by a third. I am not necessarily advocating any program along these lines, but it is interesting and perhaps important to consider the possibilities.

From all these considerations and from what is known about the possibilities of increasing food production by increasing the land under cultivation and the yield per acre, it is reasonable to conclude that it is technically possible to provide adequately for the food needs of the world for some time to come, in spite of the rapid increase of the world population now being experienced. We may deplore the population increase on many grounds and most of us believe it is important to take all possible measures that will reduce birth rates under certain conditions. But the difficult problems of feeding the world and its growing population are not technological; they are economic and political.

Optimum Rates of Population Growth

FEW men, no matter how old, ever give up seeking their ideal of feminine beauty. They also seek other ideals, such as an ideal world, or the ideal way of life. But we demographers very properly seek the ideal size or quality of population. Since most of us are apparently more concerned with size than quality, we will start with the concept of size.

It would be nice to know how many people there should be in an ideal world, an ideal continent, or an ideal community. Unfortunately there are great difficulties, as indeed there are with feminine beauty, in getting people to agree on what we should use as the standard of measure. Should it be the economic measure, the size of population that would allow the greatest per capita consumption and production of goods? Or the military measure, the size that would provide the greatest military protection? Or the measure of scholarly activity, or leisure-time recreation, or any of the other things that for one or the other of us seem to make life worth while?

Furthermore, any substantial change in numbers can come about only in the quite distant future. Suppose the government of India decided that 200 million was an optimum number of people for that country instead of the present 380 million. It would take far more than a generation to bring about such a change, and by then there might be good reasons for seeking quite a different optimum.

The logical French demographer Sauvy defines the optimum population as "that which best assures the realization of a predetermined objective." [1] And he goes on to list some of the more frequently desired objectives. They may be wealth, the maximum production and con-

[1] Alfred Sauvy, *Théories Général de la Population* (Paris, 1952), Vol. 1, pp. 25–88.

sumption of goods; the speed with which wealth increases, since happiness is found more in increase than in wealth of itself; the conservation of natural resources for the use of future generations; military power, or some other form of power; full employment; health and longevity; culture, education, knowledge; the total of well-being and its optimum distribution. Others include social harmony, ideal family size, and political institutions such as are necessary for successful democracy.

To achieve agreement on what should be the optimum population size, we must first choose which of these objectives we are aiming at. Since this is a matter of values, there will be as many objectives as there are individual points of view toward life, and as many different optimums. Obviously the optimum from the point of view of military power will be very different from the optimum from the point of view of say, social harmony, or total well-being. It would be desirable to agree on the proportionate weight to be given to each of a number of objectives, and develop in this way a kind of average optimum. But this would be difficult because there are so many different values, each given different weight by different persons.

The objective of economic well-being is probably the one on which Americans would find the most agreement. It is also easier to measure than the other objectives.

If we use the economic objective, then the optimum population would be that which made possible the greatest production and the greatest consumption of goods per person. Obviously the optimum number of people would depend on the state of the culture and the technical arts, the number and kind of tools available, and the available natural resources. When the only mode of life was hunting and raising a little corn, fewer than fifty thousand American Indians lived a precarious existence in our northeastern states, which now support many millions at a high level.

In 1945 Gottlieb, in the context of the state of the arts then existing, wrote: "Even a scanty knowledge of the known density requisites of modern industrialism and the range and caliber of our natural resources would permit the statement that per capita output [in the United States] would be substantially reduced with a population of (let us say) [less than] 50 millions [or more than] 250 millions." [2] This

---

[2] Manuel Gottlieb, "The Theory of Optimum Population for a Closed Economy," *Journal of Political Economy*, 53:289 (December 1945).

statement was made only a little over a decade ago. Today we are rapidly approaching the 250 million. We hope that atomic power and other technical advances will make possible a great increase in individual production. Otherwise our level of living may decline with each further increase in population.

The wide range set by Gottlieb in 1945 could of course be narrowed by competent economic research. We might for instance find that for the state of the arts in 1945 the economic optimum should be somewhere between 100 million and 150 million people. But this would not give us the optimum for the state of the arts in 1956, let alone their state as it might be in 1966. With each marvelous improvement in the means of production, there is some increase in the theoretical optimum number of people with which maximum per capita production could be reached. In the one or two generations it would take to reach any given optimum, the optimum may change beyond recognition. This is one of the serious difficulties with the concept of an optimum.

The economic optimum cannot be thought of in terms of production alone. There is need for saving expendable natural resources for the use of future generations. We would all be horrified at the thought of using all our oil, or copper, or coal in thirty years. But how about sixty years, or ninety? How much thought have we given to the actual loss, in our own lifetime, of our great mines of high-grade iron ore in Minnesota?

Man also has social, political, emotional, and aesthetic aspirations, which are affected by density of population. It is not by chance that in densely populated countries life is little valued. When we speak of the optimum we are generally thinking in economic terms, of resources and production. But surely there are more important goals.

Even if an optimum figure could be agreed on, its practical use would be limited. People are not willing to base their immediate plans on an optimum to be reached far in the future. India and Egypt and China are examples. I take it that these countries are at present thought to be beyond their optimum of numbers, whether from the point of view of production, or political stability, or even military power. But the Indian and Egyptian and the Communist leaders of China, and the people themselves, believe that if their countries were endowed with the factories, tools, and skills of modern technology, production would catch up with population, so long as the population did not continue to grow too rapidly. Naturally under these conditions the leaders of these countries are going to try to build the factories, improve the skills, raise the level of agriculture, so that production will catch up with population. But they are not going around announcing that there are too many Indians or too many Egyptians or too many Communists. They might not stay in office long if they did. In Dickens' *Christmas Carol*, Scrooge did not strike a popular note when he refused to give to charity, pointing out that if the poor starved the surplus population would be reduced. No sensible political leader will publicly take the position that the people he represents are surplus! Besides, the goal of an optimum population is too far off for the mass of the people to work for it; it is unrelated to their immediate needs, it does not affect their interests.

We conclude then that the concept of optimum size is hard for the scientist to handle, impractical for the politician or statesman, and does not interest the people who make the actual decisions as to size of family. The concept is likely to remain as it is today, a rather vague and theoretical objective.

Fortunately there is a practical alternative to the concept of optimum size. It is the concept of an optimum rate of growth.

Rates of population growth can be obtained from actual current statistics. It is the very special business of the demographer to find out how rapidly the population is growing each year, and he can do this quite accurately. Death rates are already so low in the United States that further reductions will not much affect our rate of growth. Growth will depend almost entirely on the number of babies born each year, or if we are looking at it over a longer term, growth will depend from one generation to another on the number of children borne by each woman during her lifetime.

We can also measure quite accurately how fast our economy is growing, that is to say, the annual rate of increase in production; nor is it too difficult to find out how rapidly from year to year we are increasing the facilities of our schools and colleges to accommodate more pupils, or how rapidly we are building new and adequate housing, enlarging our social services, and doing all the other things which, taken together, determine the natural level of living.

Knowing how fast the population is growing, and how fast production and facilities are increasing, we are in a position to figure an ideal

43

rate of population growth. If more babies are born than we are taking care of with increases in production and facilities, if we are using up our resources faster than we are renewing them or finding substitutes, we will be going backwards a little every year; we will be exceeding the optimum.

The ideal or optimum rate of growth in population must therefore be lower than the actual rate of increase in the goods and services sought after by the population. The more the increase in production of goods exceeds the increase in production of babies the greater the improvement in living from year to year. But we probably could not fix the ideal rate at a point below that required for replacing the population from one generation to another. Few people would be willing to envisage an actual decline in their numbers, and it would take the fear of a great diminution in resources, such as to threaten their future existence, before people would agree that the ideal rate should be below replacement.

There are thus quite measurable and definite upper and lower limits within which we can find an optimum rate of growth. And these limits can be derived from measurable, currently available information. For example, if production and facilities are growing at the rate of 3 per cent each year, the ideal rate of population increase will be below 3 per cent, but not below zero. How much it should be below 3 per cent will depend on some of the considerations we have to take into account in the concept of optimum numbers, but in the case of optimum growth they are understandable, and may be closely related to people's immediate interests.

When they have at hand effective means of family limitation, most couples decide on how many children they will have on the basis of their immediate personal interests: the advantages or the handicaps of a larger family, the value they assign to children as compared to alternative interests. They are influenced by the attitudes and habits of their neighbors and all the psychological pressures of their environment. Their aggregate decisions determine the rate of growth of the population. Ideal rates of growth are closer and more understandable than any ideal of an optimum population.

To the social scientist, also, an optimum rate of growth is a more practical and useful tool than the optimum gross number. He is not forced to estimate what will be the technical advances in the next generation or so, or how much a people's values will change in the same time. He can base his per capita production of goods on current and available figures. He can base his rates of increases in production on trends for the years immediately preceding. He does not have to guess what people's values will be a generation from now — he can observe them currently. In a general sort of way, values are actually measured for him in the market place. In the market place, at any given time, human values are competing with each other. Some people devote all their time and energies to the production of goods in order to satisfy a need for greater wealth. Others devote a substantial proportion of their time to recreation, others to the arts, others to the needs of their children. We Americans a generation ago spent far more time on production than we do today. When I was a boy, the ten-hour day and five-and-a-half-day week were almost universal. Today we have a forty-hour week and are talking about thirty hours. Partly this is because so many of our physical needs are satisfied, and we are able to enjoy other things. But the proportion of time spent on productive activities is not necessarily related to level of living; we may be changing our values. The people of Bali spend far more of their time than we do on the arts, even though their physical level of living is far lower than ours. Their sense of values is different from ours, and this difference finds expression in the proportion of time spent on the smaller production of goods.

Thus the proportion of time and energy spent on production as against other activities is to a considerable extent a measure of human values at any particular time. Capital put into cultural facilities, and labor diverted into services, competes with capital needed for construction of plants to increase production. The public, through the government and through private effort, will decide the priorities, and in doing so will give practical expression to a general consensus of values more meaningful than any theoretical consensus used in figuring the optimum population.

The social scientist, having available figures on current production, and through them having also some measured index of current human values, finds the concept of optimum rates of growth far more workable than the concept of an optimum size.

To the scientist the optimum rate of growth is a practical concept because he can work with it. To the political leader it is practical because he can make clear to his people that a rate of growth less than the increase in production will make them better off. And it is practical because actual birth rates are determined not only by physical circumstances at any given time, but also by habits, customs, laws, and attitudes which change with the changing needs of society. All societies make a conscious effort to change their social influences in ways thought to be desirable. To control these influences so that they will have the desired effect on birth rates is as much the function of a rational society as is the control of the things which influence production, or public health, or education, and, I believe, is just as practical.

Actual rates of growth can be brought into line with desired ideal rates without placing any outside or arbitrary controls on parents. The first steps are to give individual couples the means of limiting the size of their families, and at the same time to provide conditions under which children will not of themselves be an impossible economic handicap. Parents must be free, in the full sense of the word, to determine how many children they will have, if rate of growth is to be a voluntary process. These steps alone are likely to move birth rates nearer to ideal rates of growth.

In India, the people are not able to approach an ideal rate of growth because family limitation is not yet a part of their mores, and as a practical matter they have no means of limiting births which is sufficiently acceptable, sufficiently effective in their present circumstances, and cheap enough to be available. In the United States the effective use of contraception is still far from universal, and for couples who want larger families the costs and difficulties of raising children under urban conditions are serious handicaps. Even in the United States parents are not completely free to have the number of children they would like to have.

Voluntary family limitation can be made possible for the whole population by wider knowledge of present means of contraception, by improving methods now in use, and ultimately, we hope, by finding new physiological means of fertility control that will be wholly acceptable and effective. Economic handicaps to raising children under urban conditions can be reduced by a number of means already approved for quite other reasons. Income-tax exemptions for parents with children under eighteen were fixed when the dollar was worth two or three times its present value. The exemptions should be raised to be a real help to parents. The costs of medical care should not bear so heavily on middle-class families. Education at the college and graduate level should not be as limited as it is now to upper-income families. And so on through a whole list of economic means.

But family limitation and economic measures are not of themselves enough to ensure ideal rates of reproduction. Social and psychological influences are almost equally important. Some of these will immediately come to mind, such as the early influence of home and school on the values people set on having children, and on their responsibilities toward their children. There are many such influences. A whole science of theory, experiment, and application must be developed by our social scientists and planners. The job is no more difficult than many they have already set their hands to. The goal is most important to the well-being of the generations now being born as well as to man's long-term future.

We conclude then that rates of growth are a practical and useful concept. But it is not enough to provide a rate of growth that will protect our resources and make for steady improvement in our level of living. We must have in mind those rates of growth that will make for the improvement of our social inheritance, and even of our genetic inheritance. In other words, we must be concerned with the effect of growth on the quality of our population.

To some of us it seems strange that the social scientist has been more interested in the optimum of size than in the optimum of quality. To us quality seems the more important. It is also less difficult to handle. We can all agree on certain measurable characteristics of quality such as good health, longevity, absence of defect, intelligence, vitality, absence of antisocial qualities, and resistance to disease. These are qualities desirable for the whole population. Beyond that we need not seek agreement, except agreement that the greatest possible variety is desirable. This large world has place for every variety of useful persons: musicians, mathematicians, acrobrats, scholars, nature lovers, priests and parsons, factory workers, gadgeteers, aviators, channel swimmers, prophets, seers; plain productive businessmen, inventors, and astronomers; salesmen, columnists, editorial writers, and social scientists. We need them all. Nor need we decide the proportion of each. We can leave that to chance, as fate and natural leanings may decide. But in the optimum of size, where the optimum for one value competes with the optimum for another, there is no such leeway. Someone would have to figure out how many we would want of each kind.

If we could raise the level of good health, intelligence, and the other general qualities we have mentioned to the level at present achieved by the top 5 per cent of the population in these qualities, what a different and happier world we would be living in! We in the United States are trying to do this, and we have been trying for a long time, through more and better education, improved medical care, higher standards of nutrition, and all the other things on which we spend so much time, money, and effort. We are actuated by the fine American ideal that every person should have an equal opportunity in our society, no matter where he is born or who his parents are. We note with pride and a particular affection the man who has risen from the log cabin to the Presidency, or from newsboy to the head of a big company. Under this ideal we have come closer than most to building an ideal form of society. But there is room for doubt as to whether we have been equally successful at raising the general quality of our people. There are still too many who lack good health, vitality, or intelligence, or who are antisocial, or victims of physical or mental defect. And even our expensive and universal system of education has not trained us adequately in the virtues of citizenship. Some force must be offsetting our efforts. If too many of our children are being born in homes which give them neither affection nor intelligent care, the poor quality of their early environments might well offset all the other advantages we try so hard to give them. Our whole social inheritance would suffer a gradual deterioration.

We give little thought to what homes children are born in, even though we know that early home influences are the most important of all environmental influences, and that, on the whole, children tend to be like their parents in a wide range of characteristics. It seems to me that this is a weakness in our thinking, and that demographers are particularly guilty in this respect.

There has been little research in this field. We know in a general way that in the United States today a disproportionately large number of children are born in the homes that are at the lowest economic level; that on the average parents who have gone only through grade school have more children than those who have gone through high school, and they in turn more children than parents who have gone through

48

college. But we have no adequate knowledge of the quality of the child environment offered by these different kinds of families, nor have we any real knowledge of the numbers of children in the different kinds of families within each of these different groups. This kind of information is obtainable and we should get it. When this information is gathered we will know better how much differential rates of growth are changing the quality of our population from one generation to another, and whether for better or for worse. The present best guess is that birth differentials are a force for the worse, and that this may be at present offsetting to a large extent the forces for improvement we are working so hard to develop.

If, then, we are concerned with attaining a population of optimum quality, we must be concerned with optimum rates of differential growth; that is, rates of growth as between different kinds of families. But neither the scientist nor the public at large seems ready to work toward the moderate social changes which would bring about, quite unconsciously, a better distribution of births. The subject, rather than the proposals themselves, seems to arouse hostile emotions. People apparently feel that all such suggestions are undemocratic; that they are opposed to our ideals of equality, that someone is proposing to interfere with liberty and personal rights. These emotional reactions won't stand up if the matter is given some thought. It is not undemocratic to equalize the opportunities for having or not having children. Indeed it seems the reverse of democracy to deny access to birth control to some people, or to impose on others impossible financial handicaps if they have large families and want to give them decent care. Nor is there any suggestion that any family should be deprived of liberty or personal rights to have as many children as they want, or as few. Anything that is considered, and indeed all that would be practical and effective, should be on a wholly voluntary basis. We should provide social conditions under which the natural choice of parents as to size of family could be followed in practice, and we should provide psychological pressures in the environment which would tend to result in responsible parents having a larger proportion of the children born each year.

I cannot discuss here the measures which might be developed to promote more children among the parents who would give their children affection and intelligent care, and measures which would make for fewer children among the less responsible parents. Specific measures must wait on observation, research, and experiment. There is no doubt in my mind that practical and effective means can be found.

Today many conservationists are urging that our population is already too large. Agricultural experts are countering that we could feed many more people than we now have in this country. The argument as to what should be the optimum population does not seem to be getting us anywhere. The public is confused, and tends to accept the business view that an increase in population means more customers, more factories, more prosperity.

Instead of discussing the theory of an optimum size of population, we should consider the practical problem of actual present rates of growth. We might then discover that since the war people have been having children in far greater numbers than we have been building schools to educate them in, or houses to bring them up in, or recreation areas, roads, parks for them to enjoy themselves in. We might find that to provide these things in amounts sufficient to keep up with present birth rates, we would have to lower our level of living in other respects. We might also find that the influence of our homes was not keeping pace with the increase in children; that too many children are still being born in homes which give them less than average affection and care, and too few in the smaller number of homes where they would get more than the average of affection and wise bringing up; and that as a result, our whole social inheritance is deteriorating from one generation to the next.

We might even find that since the time when deaths were still an important factor in natural selection, a matter perhaps of the last hundred years, an adverse selection of births has been a deteriorating influence on our genetic inheritance; that there are a few less really able people being born in each generation.

If we found these things to be the case, we might then say to ourselves: We are not looking for an increase in the size and number of our factories; we don't even place per capita consumption of goods at the top in our order of priorities. We care most about a better life for our people in all its aspects. We had better slow down our rate of growth and give ourselves a chance to catch up on all these values. This is a position about which I think there would be little argument. It will come when we stop arguing about optimum populations, and think of the prospects of future generations in terms of rates of growth — something which scientists can come to agreement on; something which the public can understand and which is to their immediate interest; something which can be put into practical effect. And most of all something in which all the values of life are most likely to be given full consideration.

The Man-Land Ratio

THE concept *man-land ratio* is used in measuring the relations between a human group and its habitat. This ratio, taken by itself, is an exact and objective statement. However, it is frequently used as a means to determine the degree of population pressure. Is India overpopulated, is Thailand underpopulated, has Sweden perhaps achieved its optimum density? Obviously, answers to these questions must take into account man's activity in his physical environment. Formerly thinkers trustingly conceived of mankind and the earth as forming a harmonious balance, ordained by the Creator. But in European thought of the last century and a half there has been increasing concern regarding this relationship. At first the problem was seen as population increase outrunning food production. More recently there has been added the fear that production may decrease because man, as a poor steward, actually destroys his patrimony. Against this double-barreled pessimism voices have been raised expressing the view that man, by control over himself as well as over nature, will somehow create a new equilibrium at a higher level of human welfare.

COMPLEXITY OF THE CONCEPT

The man-land ratio expresses neatly the modern emphasis on statistical-mathematical procedure. But the exact method can give correct answers only on precise, well-defined questions. Here lies the difficulty: what is "man," and what is "land"? "Man" is the consumer but also the producer, and in each role he is different in terms of time and place. Man is not an economic abstraction. Peoples each have their own specific social organization, and their own attitudes toward the use of their

52

homeland. Villagers in India would rather lose field crops and fruits than kill cattle or monkeys. In Great Britain the social prestige of the hunter conflicts with the needs of agriculture.

It is equally difficult to define land. The Iranian nomad and the Egyptian peasant differ greatly in their notions of adequate space. Land in California meant something quite different to the Indian acorn gatherer and to the Spanish cattle rancher, and both attitudes vary greatly from that of today's real estate man. The term *Lebensraum* was — and is — open to several interpretations. By land, do we mean only "soil" producing food and organic raw materials? Does land include all local resources from climate and water to metals and fossil fuels? And should land appraisal also consider relative location — that is, accessibility?

This seemingly clear-cut man-land ratio becomes ever more involved the more one thinks about it. Classical economists replaced the "man-nature" relation by "labor-land" and added a third factor — "capital." For our approach we should use a broader term than *capital*. The word *culture*, taken as the total complex of a people's ideals and norms, social organization and technology, is certainly preferable. Thus, culture is the link, the intermediary between man and land. Each particular culture acts as a filter or a prism through which a people views its habitat. It conditions the use that a group makes of its physical environment. It determines for each society which elements of the land have value — that is, what are *resources*. No one has more clearly expounded the relativity of the resource concept than Professor Erich Zimmermann.[1]

For the moment it suffices to draw two conclusions from these remarks: First, the man-land ratio involves a very large and exceedingly complex number of elements. And, second, a meaningful approach to the problem must proceed by regions or countries. It is my purpose to review here some of the yardsticks that have been proposed to measure the man-land ratio.

CRUDE POPULATION DENSITY

The simplest expression of the man-land ratio is the number of people per unit of land area. For the earth as a whole this works out at an average of 45 people per square mile, about the density for the United States as well as for Minnesota — 14 acres per head of popula-

[1] Erich W. Zimmermann, *Resources and Industries* (New York, 1st edition, 1933, 2nd edition, 1951).

tion. A glance at a world map of population distribution, however, shows how unevenly the 2,700 million are spread over the earth. The high density realms are mainly in the moist rimlands of east and south Asia and in Europe. Additional areas of high concentration are in Java, Egypt, and eastern United States (See Table 1.)

The population distribution roughly corresponds to broad climatic regions. The areas too cold for crops (polar regions and subpolar forests) occupy one fifth of the earth's land surface. They contain less than 1 per cent of the world's population. The arid and semiarid climates cover one third of the land and have 6 per cent of the total population. The year-around wet and warm equatorial regions form close to one tenth of the land and have 2 per cent of the population. Together these areas

Table 1. Man-Land Ratios in Representative Countries

Country	Crude Density in Number of Inhabitants per Square Mile	Arable Land in Acres per Capita	Agricultural Land in Acres	
			per Capita	per Agricultural Worker
U.S.A.	54.6	3.0	7.0	153.0
Canada	5.2	6.6	10.3	151.9
Argentina	18.2	4.1	22.1	220.6
Uruguay	36.4	2.0	15.1	...
Mexico	39.0	1.7	11.3	44.6
Puerto Rico	652.6	0.3	0.6	6.3
Jamaica	345.8	0.3	0.7	4.5
Australia	2.6	5.5	117.3	1914.8
New Zealand	20.8	0.6	17.8	240.9
United Kingdom	637.0	0.4	1.0	39.9
Denmark	267.8	1.6	1.9	15.1
Netherlands	852.8	0.2	0.6	7.7
France	202.8	1.2	2.1	11.2
Poland	221.0	1.7	2.1	14.6
Yugoslavia	176.8	1.2	2.3	6.8
Bulgaria	176.8	1.4	1.6	4.1
Spain	148.2	1.7	3.7	22.3
U.S.S.R.	26.0	2.7	4.2	...
Egypt	57.2	0.3	0.3	1.4
Gold Coast	52.0	3.3	4.7	...
Kenya	26.0	0.7	6.4	...
India	299.0	0.9	0.9	5.1
Malaya	117.0	1.0	1.0	4.5
Philippines	187.2	0.5	1.2	2.9
China	156.0	0.5	1.5	...
Japan	618.8	0.2	0.1	0.9

Source: U.N. Food and Agriculture Organization, *Yearbook 1954*, Vol. VIII, Part 1; U.N., *Demographic Yearbook*, 1955.

of climatic handicaps cover almost two thirds of the earth's land surface but support less than one tenth of the world's population. Possibly the future may witness a greater settlement in these sectors, but the fact that man in thousands of years has only partly mastered them indicates the severity of the challenge. We have only to think of our recurrent droughts and dust storms in the Great Plains to realize that modern technology has not solved the problem.

The remaining lands are in the seasonally wet subtropics and the so-called temperate humid lands. Here, on one third of the land surface, live nine tenths of the world's population. Obviously physical environmental factors greatly affect the earth's carrying capacity. Even if we assume equal cultural conditions, the man-land ratio for Ohio is bound to be very different from that of Nevada, or the Ukraine from that of northern Siberia.

At first sight the proportion of farmland to population appears to be a fair yardstick for measuring the pressure a nation exerts on its resources. Let us look at the facts. According to F.A.O. statistics 3,000 million acres, 9 per cent of the land surface, are in use as arable land for field crops and orchards. In addition 5,300 million acres, 16 per cent of the land surface, are used as meadows and permanent pastures. If we add arable land, meadows, and pastures together we have 8,300 million acres of what we shall call agricultural land, a quarter of the land surface. This means that the average world citizen has 3.3 acres of agricultural land, of which slightly more than 1 acre is arable. These figures are, of course, mere theory because they presuppose a One World unity. It is more realistic to examine how much arable land each country has per head of total population (see Table 1 and Figure 1).

It is a popular belief that teeming millions, crowded in space, spell poverty: the less arable land there is per inhabitant the lower the level of living. In the United States we have 3 acres of arable land per capita, Canada has twice as much, and Australia is between these two. It is certainly true that these three countries enjoy a high standard of living. For contrast one might compare the countries with half an acre or less of arable land per capita. In Asia these include such countries as China, the Philippines, and Ceylon, each with 0.5 acre, Korea with 0.4 acre, and Japan with less than 0.2 acre per capita. (The data for India indi-

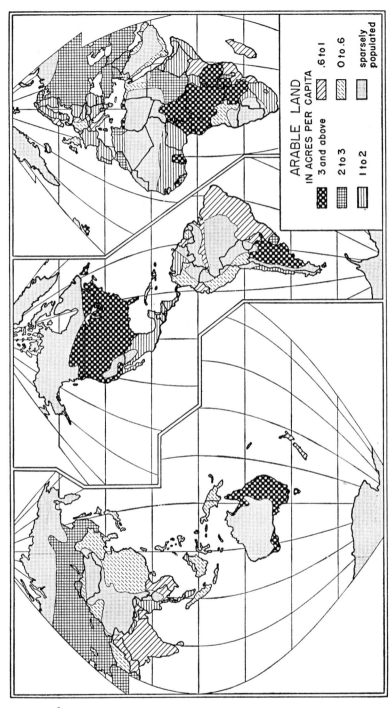

Figure 1. Arable land (including treecrops, fallow, and land temporarily used for pasture) in acres per capita. Based on U.N. Food and Agriculture Organization, Yearbook 1954, Vol. VIII, Part 1. Base map copyright by Rand McNally & Company, R.L. 58 S 8.

ARABLE LAND
IN ACRES PER CAPITA

3 and above
2 to 3
1 to 2
.6 to 1
0 to .6
sparsely populated

cate 0.9 acre per capita, a rather high figure, which may be due to a different classification of arable land.) In the Western Hemisphere Haiti, Puerto Rico, and Jamaica, each with 0.3 acre, are in the lowest category. There is no denying that these countries are, on the whole, poor. The thesis seems proved! But a glance at western Europe shatters the naive hypothesis. Here are several countries with less than half an acre of arable land per inhabitant: the United Kingdom and West Germany (both with 0.4 acre), Belgium and Switzerland (0.3), and the Netherlands (0.2). In material wealth they are certainly "upper middle class" when compared with the countries mentioned in Asia and the Caribbean. It is interesting to note that in Europe there is a gradient of increasing ratios of arable land as one goes east or south from western Europe, while levels of living generally decrease in the same direction. (Poland has 1.7 acres per capita, Bulgaria 1.4, the Soviet Union 2.7, Spain 1.7.)

The ratios are, of course, somewhat different if one considers all agricultural land including meadows and permanent pastures. Yet the over-all picture remains the same. However interesting these comparisons are, they do not by themselves give us an adequate yardstick to measure population pressure. They certainly warn us not to jump to conclusions regarding the amount of land needed for a satisfactory standard of welfare.

PRODUCTIVITY

Each year there are more mouths to be fed and fed better, but expansion of farm land is difficult. This points up the need for greater production per unit of land. A worldwide comparison of annual yields per acre, expressed in calories, would tell us which nations make the best use of their land for this purpose. Unfortunately the data are quite scarce. From what we know it appears that western Europe is at the top, producing perhaps 7,500 original calories per acre. East and south Asia are in the middle,[2] while Anglo-America and Australia rank low. If one took western Europe as the standard for intensity of food production per unit of land, the earth could feed many more millions. Especially the technologically advanced countries such as the United States and Canada, and also Argentina and the Soviet Union, could

[2] This refers, of course, to the average. Within this realm Japan ranks high, India quite low.

support much larger populations by aiming at the highest possible yields per acre.

This brings us to a dilemma: should we judge by efficiency in output per land unit or by efficiency in output per man-hour? The most economic use of land appears wasteful of labor, and the most economic use of labor is likely to be wasteful of land. The present farmers of western Europe seem to have found a rather successful compromise between the two extremes. Their income level is, on the average, satisfactory. But many agrarian countries have a very low productivity per worker, which is the main reason for their poverty.

Low productivity per worker means that each can handle only a small area. The size of agricultural land per farm worker gives us some insight into the economic use of labor. At the one extreme we have Australia with 1,915 acres of agricultural land, mostly pastures, per head of those agriculturally employed. New Zealand (with 241 acres), Argentina (221), and the United States (153) can also be considered to be in the top group, particularly if one restricts the comparison to arable land. At the other extreme are countries with less than 5 acres of agricultural land per worker. These we find particularly in eastern and southern Asia, in the Middle East, and also in southeast Europe. Although Africa and Latin America seem well off in agricultural land per farm worker, this is less so if only arable land is considered. The prevailing simple hoe agriculture demands the use of a large labor force.

It appears that most so-called underdeveloped countries have too many people on the land. In other words, the use of labor is uneconomical. This would show up even better if we had worldwide data for production of original calories per farm worker. From what is known, it seems that in Anglo-America one farm worker produces two to three times as many calories as his counterpart does in western Europe and ten to fifteen times as much as the farm worker in east and south Asia.

BEYOND AGRICULTURE

In the underdeveloped and densely populated countries the first need certainly is greater food production. But to raise the level of living requires also increased productivity per worker. This is easier said than done. Mechanization is virtually impossible on the small farm plots of India, Java, or China. And even if this, or other labor-saving methods, were possible, what would one then do with the surplus of agricultural labor? Industrialization is the obvious answer, but sales of manufactured goods will be small as long as purchasing power is low. If this is not a vicious circle, it is at best a spiral road that climbs very slowly toward higher levels of living.

The distance to be traveled can be illustrated by comparing various indices of economic development (see Table 2). A very illuminating yardstick is the consumption of commercial energy per capita in different countries. Here we see clearly how the control over "mechanical slaves" gives the worker in the industrial-commercial countries the edge over his counterpart in the underdeveloped countries. This again translates itself fairly well in levels of income, steel consumption, and daily food intake. (See Figures 2 and 3.)

Table 2. Consumption per Capita for Representative Countries

Country	Inanimate Energy Consumption per Capita in Metric Tons of Coal Equivalent	Calorie Intake per Capita per Day	Steel Consumption in Pounds per Capita
U.S.A.	7.62	3,090	1,052
Canada	6.88	3,030	603
Argentina	0.88	2,800	174
Uruguay	0.75	2,950	145
Mexico	0.65	...	53
Puerto Rico	0.66	...	..
Jamaica	0.29	...	..
Australia	3.67	3,290	664
New Zealand	2.62	3,340	365
United Kingdom	4.78	3,140	713
Denmark	2.17	3,280	367
Netherlands	2.07	2,910	458
France	2.49	2,795	464
Poland	(0.75)*	...	(66)
Yugoslavia	0.47	...	101
Greece	0.33	2,520	51
Spain	0.74	...	95
Egypt	0.24	2,390	23
Gold Coast	0.11	...	..
Kenya	0.09	...	..
India	0.11	1,685	13
Malaya	0.32	...	66
Philippines	0.10	...	24
China	...	...	11
Japan	0.97	2,165	158

Source: Most recent data (1952–54) as given in U.N. statistical yearbooks.
* Figures in parentheses are prewar.

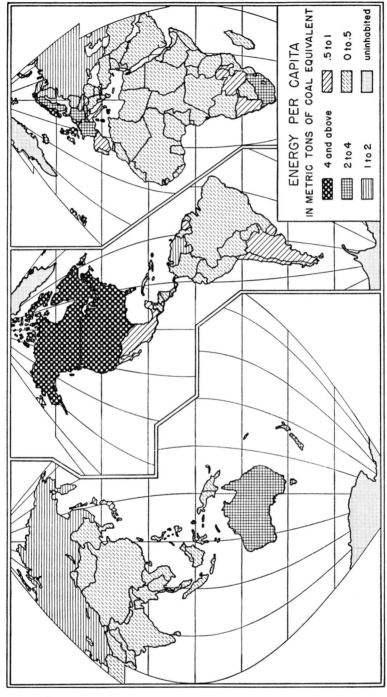

Figure 2. Estimated consumption per capita of commercial sources of energy, expressed in terms of coal, for the year 1955. Based on U.N. Statistical Yearbook 1956. Base map copyright by Rand McNally & Company, R.L. 58 S 8.

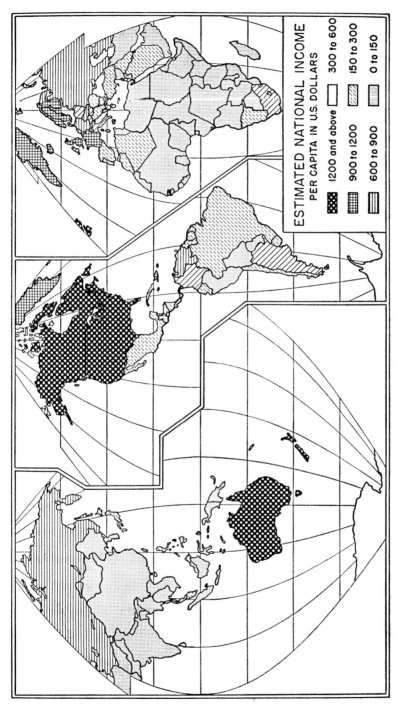

Figure 3. Estimated national income per capita. Adapted from U.N. sources and the map by N. Ginsburg in Annals Assn. Am. Geographers, Vol. 47 (1957), p. 200. Base map copyright by Rand McNally & Company, R.L. 58 S 8.

ESTIMATED NATIONAL INCOME
PER CAPITA IN U.S. DOLLARS

1200 and above   300 to 600

900 to 1200   150 to 300

600 to 900   0 to 150

The Population Ahead

Measuring what the man-land ratio *is* does not answer the question of what it *ought* to be. The latter question involves cultural values and ethical judgments that transcend the objective facts. These standards are not immutable, but they are sufficiently "set" to make change a slow process. Each culture at a given time has its own notions on the purpose of life and thus on the relations between man and his habitat. It is only in the framework of the prevailing attitudes that the objective measurements of man-land ratios can serve as guideposts to the desired goal.

THE DANGER AHEAD

In Western societies, and increasingly so in others too, the material welfare of the individual is considered to be the main dividend to be gained from the partnership between man and land. The United States and other Anglo-Saxon countries of recent settlement rank highest in this achievement. But there remains a nagging doubt. How far can we push "the twin spirals of capacity to produce and capacity to consume"? [3] Many thoughtful people warn that there is a limit, but their concern is largely with the question of how to feed an ever-increasing population. There is no denying that this is the foremost problem, and a serious one, in the present period of an "exploding" population. However, there is evidence to support the view that the increase will taper off, even in crowded Asia. If this is true the future holds an even greater problem in the rapid increase of consumption of industrial raw materials. The food consumption per capita is relatively inelastic, but the demand for other goods seems almost boundless. In the last fifty years the population of the United States has doubled, but the production of minerals has increased eight times, that of power eleven times. Most of this production is actually extraction of nonrenewable resources. [4]

It was stressed earlier that the man-land ratio must be analyzed regionally or country-wise. But we must also view each part in relation to the whole. If Los Angeles gobbles up the water from far around, it condemns some areas to eternal drought — a minor matter, perhaps. But if a few countries consume most of the metals and energy sources, the

[3] Carl O. Sauer in *Man's Role in Changing the Face of the Earth*, ed. William L. Thomas (Chicago: University of Chicago Press, 1956), p. 66.
[4] For detailed information see President's Materials Policy Commission, *Resources for Freedom*, 5 volumes (Washington, D.C.: Government Printing Office, 1952).

problem may become serious. At present the so-called well-developed countries with 25 per cent of the world's population consume 95 per cent of all mineral production. Per capita they use one hundred times as much as the underdeveloped countries do.

The rate of consumption of industrial resources is now beginning to rise in several underdeveloped countries. In time their needs will compete with ours. Technology can and will develop substitutes — at a price — but the question is whether or not the rate of new developments can keep pace with increasing demands.

∞

The Equilibrium Population

I PRESUME that the role of the biologist in this symposium is to erect a tower of ivory, or of some similar, easily carvable white substance, from which to gain perspective over the madding crowd. From this ivory, or soapen, pinnacle we can see at once that there is no such thing as a population problem; there is only population. All species are populations, by definition, and if there were no population there would be no problem — the term is therefore superfluous. Man's objective is that of all species: to maintain the population, i.e. to exist. Our old friend the "struggle for existence" is nowadays called *equilibrium* — a state of poise or balance between opposing forces. In Darwin's time the emphasis was ordinarily placed on downward displacements from equilibrium — "let him who thinketh he standeth take heed lest he fall." Today, and particularly with regard to our own species, we are more conscious of the force of procreation that opposes and may temporarily outrun the forces of destruction.

I take it that we are all intent on understanding two aspects of man's future: at what level, and when, will the equilibrium population be attained? and what can be done to cushion the economic and psychologic shocks that equilibrium will bring? Now, none of us really knows intellectually, far less do we know in our innermost subconscious, what it means to be a member of an equilibrium population. Unlike the demographer, the biologist is accustomed to populations at and above as well as below equilibrium; hence his viewpoint may be useful in considering these questions.

I propose first to deal with statics, the kind of events that can be seen from the top of the soapen tower, and then to move closer to some populations in an effort to see their kinetics, or what makes them tick without exploding. Finally I shall return to a matter of statics, the advantages and disadvantages of an oscillatory equilibrium.

The ecologist's model of community equilibrium was first sketched in some detail by a Minnesota biologist, the late Raymond Lindeman, whose field of operation was a small lake in Anoka County. In a four-year study of Cedar Log Lake, surely one of the most valuable Ph.D. theses ever done in ecology, Lindeman measured with great care the standing crops of algae, pondweeds, rotifers, copepods, insects, fish, and the like, and then proceeded with great insight to estimate their various rates of turnover in order to compute the input and use of energy of the whole aquatic community. It had been axiomatic in ecology that the *numbers* of animals at different levels in a food chain should stand in roughly pyramidal relation to each other — many springtails, fewer spiders, still fewer muddaubers, still fewer birds that eat muddaubers. What Lindeman did was to convert such numbers into *masses*, so that the plants could be included, then to turn these masses into rates of production, and then to express them in units of the chemical energy fixed by one level and handed on to the next higher level. This led him to the discovery of a fairly systematic relation, which had been suspected before but never made quantitative: while the plants on a given area used solar energy with an efficiency of the order of 0.1 per cent, the herbivores were about 10 per cent efficient in utilizing plants, and the carnivores in turn were about 10 per cent efficient in utilizing herbivores. So the theoretical figure for the growth of all carnivores on an area is 10 per cent of 10 per cent, or 1 per cent; it will not be very different if carnivores are 20 per cent efficient, as Lindeman's seemed to be, for 20 per cent of 10 per cent is only 2 per cent. We see at once why meat costs more than corn. For the same reasons the management of lake fisheries for pickerel or lake trout is an uneconomic luxury: this is an inefficient way to "grow protein."

The energetics of a land community are more difficult to work out, and in applying Lindeman's scheme to the production of human substance we have to make a number of guesses. Moreover there is a vast difference in energy requirements between a copepod and a long-lived warm-blooded large mammal such as man, and this difference was not sufficiently allowed for in my previous reports on this subject. Because the approach is more valid than the existing data, it is worth while to run through the calculations again.

To determine the cost in energy for population growth we need to know the following: How many people are added each year, at least approximately? How much do they weigh? How many calories are needed to enable a person to weigh this much? How much food must be produced to obtain this much food? These calculations require very large numbers. A shorthand way of writing big numbers is to write them as a product of a number times ten raised to a *power*. Thus 10 raised to a power gives a number which may be conventionally written as a 1 followed by the number of zeros equal to the power. In other words $10^9 = 1,000,000,000 = 1$ billion. Hence $2\frac{1}{2}$ billion may be written as $(2.5)(10^9)$; 250 as $(2.5)(10^2)$, etc.

The standing crop of human beings (those now living) is about $(2.6)(10^9)$ persons, on an average weighing 60 kilograms "fresh," or 21 kilograms "dry" (the difference being essentially the amount of water which man need not produce). The rate of production of new substance by the crop is about one twenty-fifth of the crop, since the mean life span of humans is about twenty-five years; here we write down at once the figure that is most uncertain and difficult to obtain for nonhuman species. The dry matter can be taken to be all protein, with an energy content of 5,650 calories per gram. Multiplying these factors together, we find that the new growth, what ecologists call the net productivity, represents $(1.23)(10^{13})$ calories per year. Now in order to produce this net the crop consumes a great deal of energy and spends it to maintain its bodies intact and functional — i.e. most of the fuel intake is respired away and does not appear as output. Allowing 1,690 calories per day as the metabolism of a working man of 60 kilograms average weight, the respiratory loss amounts to $(1.6)(10^{15})$ calories per year, or 130 times the energy remaining as net production. Disregarding the net output as too small to affect the figures, we can consider $(1.6)(10^{15})$ calories per year as the gross productivity, and this can be compared to the gross productivity of all plants on the terrestrial earth. The plants' net production is estimated by Schroeder as about $(1.6)(10^{17})$ calories per year, and to this we must add the 25 per cent or so that the plants spend for their own vegetable purposes, giving a gross productivity of $(2.0)(10^{17})$ calories per year. The fraction $1.6/200$ gives the efficiency of human gross production as 0.8 per cent. Let us call this about 1 per cent, and remember that 1 per cent is the theoretical figure for all carnivores referred to the plants at the base of their food chains. The calculation implies that if man were entirely a carnivore he would consume essentially all the carnivory there is or can be on land.

This result is worth some thought in the light of what we know of plant production generally. Table 1 gives a few examples of net production rates as calories per square meter per year. The really high figures represent very special circumstances, in which there is an unearned increment of energy resulting from orderly spatial arrangement. Turtle-grass communities in the Florida Keys utilize nutrients brought to them

Table 1. Some Typical Net Productivity Figures for Plant Communities

Community	Grams of Carbon per Square Meter per Day	Growing Season in Days	Number of Crops per Year	Production, in Calories per Square Meter per Year
Aquatic communities				
Turtle-grass, Florida	5	200	1	10,000
Silver Springs	8.7	200	1	17,500
Chlorella cultures	9.5	365	(1)	34,600
Lakes (Verduin)	0.36	30	10	1,000
Eutrophic lakes				
Mendota, plankton				2,920
Mendota, incl. pondweeds				3,140
Linsley Pond				1,290
W. North Atlantic (Riley)				3,400
Terrestrial communities				
Wild hay	0.71	120	2	1,700
Clover-timothy hay	1.76	80	3	8,400
Tall-grass prairie	2.36	120	2	5,680
Ragweed	4.29	150	1	6,410
Corn (U.S. average)	2.21	120	1	2,650*
Forest (Krogh)				5,000
Semi-aquatic plants				
Cattail	4.15	120	1	5,000
Water lettuce (Pistia)	6.8	100	2	13,600
Water hyacinth	6.1	60	4	14,640
Rice (U.S. average)	1.55	140	1	2,170*
Average, world's vegetation (Schroeder)				1,320

* Whole plant.

at optimal rates by warm ocean currents. The springs of Florida provide a very large flow of nutrient-rich water at a constant temperature, and the products of photosynthesis in the exceptionally clear water are removed before they cut down the light. The artificial cultures of Chlorella produce at a very high rate, but a great deal of energy is spent in supplying them with strong light and in bubbling CO_2 through the medium at an optimal rate. We see that 5,000 calories per square meter per year is the production of a good forest, of which about two thirds goes into wood and one third falls down as leaves and twigs. Lakes and the ocean in temperate latitudes are about as productive as land. The average agricultural land under conditions in the United States produces about half as much as forest, or only about one fourth as much in harvestable grain (because these figures include the whole corn and rice plant above ground). The worldwide terrestrial average, including deserts and the arctic tundra, is about one fifth as much as a good forest. Yet it is this last figure we used in computing human efficiency, and it is arithmetically convenient that agricultural products yield a like amount—about 1,000 calories per square meter per year of edible carbohydrate.

What, then, would be the consequence of increasing the human crop by ten times? Not only would meat-eating become impossible. Human productive efficiency would have to increase to 10 per cent, that of all the herbivory on earth. So the whole land area would have to be brought into production, and made to produce as much edible carbohydrate as it now produces in reindeer lichen, cactus, and tropical wood. I think I am not wrong in suggesting, therefore, that a factor of 10 is beyond the margin of safety; yet at the rate of increase of 1 per cent per year the human population will grow tenfold in 230 years.

In considering man as a carnivore, it is amusing to deal with the simplest imaginable stage, that of naked, acultural men dependent on the animal food produced by a temperate forest. The requisite data do not exist for any one forest community, but by piecing information together we can arrive at some estimates of the productivity of herbivorous animals. Snowshoe hares in the Lake Alexander district of Minnesota provide a model for procedure. The census shows that their average density over eight years is one per hectare, and adult weight is about 1.9 kilograms. The adult mortality rate is constant at 70 per cent per year, and the mean longevity is 0.93 years; the crop turns over slightly faster than annually. The net productivity in calories comes out at 410 per square meter per year. This time, to compute the gross productivity, we apply the respiratory correction to the net production, since the crop turns over more than once per year. The result is 4,170 calories per square meter per year, or about 10 times the net production; you will remember that this factor for man is 130 because of the large standing crop and the low replacement rate. Adding the net production to the respiration, we find 4,580 calories per square meter per year as the gross production of hares; about one tenth of this could actually be caught and eaten without disturbing the hares' equilibrium.

By similar methods we compute the gross production of woodmice in Michigan as 9,470 calories per square meter per year, or about twice that of hares. Birds are hardly worth the effort of catching them; about 982 calories per square meter per year is their gross productivity, and only about one thirtieth of that is catchable. Neither are deer, which is more surprising: about 780 calories per square meter per year is their gross production, and because the annual production of a herd of twenty-four deer is only five yearlings the catchable yield is much less than that of birds. Still, a deer looks big to a hungry man, and as we are forced to neglect the rabbits, squirrels, and porcupines, as well as all the edible insects and reptiles, we will do well to include the birds and deer. The total of catchable animal matter, then, comes out at 16,000 calories per square meter per year, of which about 730 calories, or less than 5 per cent, is catchable net productivity.

If we take the ratio of gross productivities as 10 per cent, 16,000 calories of animals support 1,600 calories of hunter, all but 1/130th of which goes for respiration, leaving 12.3 calories for growth. The standing crop would be about 25 times this, making the surprising total of 2.6 persons per square kilometer. But then we remember that this assumes that all the yield of catchable animals goes into human substance, leaving none for other carnivores. It seems safer to calculate from the net production of animals, and assume a physiologic conversion rate of less than 1 to 1, say 50 per cent. Then 700 calories of food support 350 calories of hunter, 2.7 calories of which go for growth. The standing crop then comes out at 0.57 persons per square kilometer, which is only about fifteen times the average density of eighteenth-century American plains Indians, as computed from Mooney's data.

A comparable average density of aboriginal hunters and gatherers is given for Australia by Birdsell, 0.03 per square kilometer as compared to the American 0.04. Presumably the factor-of-15 discrepancy between the computed and the actual human crops means that some component of the environment other than food was usually limiting. It may have been "social forces"; it may merely have been the unequal distribution of water or of salt. But we should note that a fifteen-fold margin of safety is not a serious discrepancy, since the figures are based on averages. We know that the snowshoe hare crop varies over a ten-year cycle with the maximum density at least fifteen times the minimum density; but I shall show that this variability is probably a property of hares, not of the environment, and presumably the Indians would find a shift to woodmice rewarding in years when hares were scarce. More to the point is the observation that Australian aboriginal populations varied from tribe to tribe by a factor of more than 200. At maximum departure from the average density a tribe must certainly be pressing hard on its food supply, and a variance of fifteen-fold within which oscillations are possible without disturbing the normal environment is probably to be thought of as the least that the real situation requires.

This discussion tends to raise the question of oscillatory equilibria, which I prefer to reserve for later consideration, after I have treated some matters of kinetics. Let me summarize the statics of energy balance by making these points:

1. For a hunting and gathering economy, average density is about 0.04 person per square kilometer; the energy balance suggests that this figure can be increased locally by about twenty times, say to 1 per square kilometer, or even higher if much plant food is gathered.

2. For an agricultural economy, optimal density, considering increased productivity of land and increased efficiency of exploitation of vegetable food, is about 100–300 per square kilometer. Typical densities at this stage, however, are 400 per square kilometer (Java) or 600 per square kilometer (Egypt). At this level human productivity is maximal, but the standard of living is low.

3. For an industrial-agricultural economy, such as the United States, density is 20 per square kilometer; the worldwide average is also 20 per square kilometer. A slight increase in productivity of agricultural land does not compensate for the proportion of land removed for other purposes or simply not exploited.

4. At the tenfold increase level, worldwide population density would

be 200 per square kilometer. Population needs for food alone require either that all men become exclusively herbivorous, dependent on worldwide plant production at its present value, or that the average production of agricultural land be increased by ten times. Edible grains are not efficient enough to permit this, nor are forest trees; the food plant of the future appears to be either Chlorella or water hyacinth.

INCREASE AND LONGEVITY

It is customary to begin discussions of population dynamics in general by writing down the Pearl-Verhulst logistic equation for population growth:

$$\frac{dN}{dt} = bN\left(\frac{K-N}{K}\right)$$

where dN/dt is the rate of change of numbers (N) with respect to time (t), b is the constant of maximal potential increase, and $(K-N)/K$ is a density corrective, expressing the fact that growth is slowed increasingly as N approaches saturation (K).

I find this equation to be a useful teaching device. However, although it is commonly used to describe growth, it is often sterile. The trouble is that an "S" curve of this kind "fits," or describes, one set of data but leads to impossible inferences. For example, to a mathematically oriented theorist, it seems to imply that birth and death rates are essentially describable by a straight line. Ecologists have begun to raise questions about the possible interaction of birth and death rates; it would be no surprise to find that demographers have, too. At any rate, students of population, professional or not, will find that biologists have instructive as well as interesting comments to make.

Although no sociologist can do likewise, the biologist can create a situation of "unlimited food supply." Removing the effects of having to search for food is equal to removing from consideration any effect of *density* of population as such. In such a situation, the population grows in what may be termed a "snowball" — each succeeding period being dependent upon the population of the preceding population. To use mathematical symbols, dN/dt = rN, where N refers to "Numbers," "t" refers to "time," and "r" refers to "rate." This "r" turns out to be the rate of growth that Malthus talked about; for the geometric growth that disturbed Malthus is simply a "snowballing" growth. Since birth

Table 2. Reproductive Potentiality of Several Animals

Animal	Intrinsic Rate of Natural Increase (r)	Mean Length of a Generation (T)	Rate of Multiplication per Generation (R_0)
Daphnia	0.8 per day	6.8 days	221.5
Pond snail	0.02–0.04 per day	124–246 days	ca. 450.0
Body louse	0.111 per day	30.92 days	30.93
Flour beetle	0.707 per week	7.9 weeks	275.0
Rice weevil	0.76 per week	6.2 weeks	113.6
Rat	0.103 per week	31.0 weeks	25.66
Vole	0.088 per week	20.2 weeks	5.90
Man (Egypt)	ca. 0.012 per year	28 years	ca. 1.4

and death rates in human populations are not freed from density, Dublin and Lotka's figure of 5 per thousand per year for the United States in 1920 is not comparable with data for experimental animals. Nevertheless, I have entered a similar value for Egypt in Table 2.

In Table 2, the constant r gives the instantaneous rate of increase, what Lotka calls the *intrinsic rate of natural increase*. To find out what this means in terms of a finite rate of multiplication we need the mean length of a generation, shown in the next column; the last column shows R_0, the rate of multiplication per head per generation. All these figures are to be found in the literature except those for the water flea Daphnia, which I have computed from some rough figures of my own to show what an animal can do. These values are possible because the population consists entirely of parthenogenetic females that bring forth ten to thirty live young every time they moult, which is about every second day through adult life.

These figures, of course, show potentialities only; r represents maximum births minus minimum deaths. For real populations living in real environments the effect of increasing N is to make the death rate increase and the birth rate decrease until, at equilibrium, $dN/dt = 0$. We can infer, then, that deaths vary as some positive function of N, while births vary as a negative function of N. When these relationships are examined graphically they prove invariably to be non-linear, to require a curved rather than a straight line. The most interesting cases are those where the effect of density is not even monotonic — i.e. the natality (or mortality) may both increase and decrease with density.

EDWARD S. DEEVEY

As an example that is reasonably well understood, we may take the case of Tribolium, the flour beetle. Two pairs per 32 grams of flour increase faster than one pair, and four pairs increase faster than two pairs. Above a density of four pairs the natality falls again. The explanation is that fertility increases with repeated matings, at least up to a point; one or two pairs per 32 grams of flour is too rarefied a population for females to meet males often enough for adequate insemination. But as the opportunity for encounters increases, there is also opportunity for the adults and larvae to meet the defenseless eggs and pupae, which they do not distinguish from bits of flour. So we find that there is an optimum density for fecundity, both lower and higher densities being deleterious.

An optimum density also exists for mortality in Daphnia and in the fruit fly Drosophila. The probable explanation here is that some of the organisms introduced into the non-sterile cultures required in the experiment are deleterious, and may get out of hand if they are not grazed down rapidly enough; yet they must be introduced along with the food organisms. At densities too low for the wild organisms to be kept in check the mortality of the Daphnia or Drosophila is increased; at higher densities the mortality is less; but at still higher densities the animals begin to affect each other adversely (through excretory products or through physical contact) and the mortality increases again.

The great biologic importance of the conditions under which optimum density may occur is that they provide the raw material for the evolution of sociality; they give natural selection something to get hold of, a slight initial advantage of aggregation over random dispersion that can be improved upon as sociality becomes more and more elaborate in its repercussions. But I cannot here explore this point, and I will merely remark that we do not know what the optimum density is for man today, but that in the past it clearly lay at some value below that found in cities. If one takes the archaeologic data for deaths at particular ages, and uses them (swallowing some outrageous assumptions) to compute life tables, one finds that mean longevity in Bronze Age Anatolia was markedly greater than for urban classical Greece or Rome. Even the hunters and gatherers of Mesolithic times appear to have lived as long as the ancient Romans on the average. The enhanced death rates characteristic of cities are intuitively obvious despite the difficulties of proving them statistically. The downward trend of mean longevity

73

with urbanization is something that has begun to be corrected only recently, and in a few Western cities; Calcutta must be as unlikely a place in which to live a long life as ancient Rome was.

LONGEVITY OF ANIMALS IN NATURE

This brings me to life tables for natural populations of animals. Since we seldom want to insure the life of a robin or a vole, it is not worth while to compute their life tables with rigor. Moreover, it is obvious that mean longevity depends heavily on density, so survivorship curves showing death rates for specified ages can vary enormously, even in theory. But the pattern of survival probably varies less than do the values of its constants, and inasmuch as we deal with populations at or near equilibrium densities, we can learn much from the changing force of mortality with age.

If every age group is as likely to suffer death as every other, the mortality rate with age is a constant fraction. Since multiplying by a constant fraction is equivalent to subtracting a constant logarithm, a graph of logarithm of survivors against age produces a straight diagonal line when no age is a more favored time of dying. Oversimplifying the situation considerably, we can say that secure laboratory populations of most invertebrates — Hydra, rotifers, Daphnia, insects — display little variation from this diagonal straight-line form. And there is no good reason why such animals should do so: they have little or no power to learn, and so to avoid death, and their life span in typical environments is never more than a small fraction of their physiologic maximum. A change in their way of life, as when an insect metamorphoses or a pelagic oyster larva settles down, will usually mean a quite different environment in respect to the chances of death; but the consequence is usually to substitute for one straight-line mortality curve another of different slope.

To say this is not to imply that invertebrates have no behavior to substitute for intelligence. Pelagic larvae of the tubeworm Spirorbis have a battery of adaptive but quasi-automatic responses that permit them to settle down and become adult in localities favorable for tubeworms. At a certain age they avoid the light and seek the bottom of the estuary, where they crawl about. If they receive no stimulus from another settled tubeworm they seek the light and swim once more, thus being wafted upstream or downstream by the tide. Periodically they

74

descend and rise again, testing the substratum until they make contact with another tubeworm, whereupon they settle at once nearby. The drive to settle can be increased by preventing them from settling. Again, so witless an animal as a barnacle can also be shown to be gregarious when settling out of the plankton; Knight-Jones has found that cyprid larvae of *Balanus balanoides*, which has a membranous base of attachment when adult, respond specifically on contact to a tanned protein that is present in the base and shell of adults and also in the larval shells. So they settle and grow up only where there are other barnacles, a situation that favors survival and the cross-fertilization that is probably necessary. But an adaptive variance has been built into the process, to ensure that newly favorable habitats are eventually colonized: *B. balanoides* rarely settles on smooth glass, but when it does it at once makes the glass attractive to other settling larvae.

Survival throughout the life span has not been critically studied in these species, but in the sessile rotifer Floscularia Edmondson showed that the mean longevity is approximately doubled for individuals that settle at the base or on the tube of an older individual. Floscularia lives by preference on the leaves of a floating water plant, the bladderwort Utricularia, but shows a statistical predilection for the oldest viable leaves, whereas another species, *Collotheca gracilipes*, affects the youngest leaves and is specifically attracted by an organic substance extractable from them. The plant grows forward at the tip and dies back at the base, as does the floating seaweed Sargassum, and the interaction between community dynamics and population dynamics in these stably unstable substrata poses problems in moving equilibria that Alice's Red Queen might have understood, but as yet no ecologist does.

When we come to birds and mammals we expect the interplay between life and death to wear a different aspect, for the higher animals are more like ourselves, more capable of learning, and many of them are at least incipiently social. But oddly enough, in adult birds at any rate, experience of life seems not to teach ways of avoiding death. A great variety of species have been studied, usually from banding returns, and all prove to have essentially constant mortality rates from the first year onward. And in one social species, the herring gull, Paynter's studies of juvenile mortality suggest that sociality is not an unmixed blessing. Gulls in a large gullery (the Kent Island colony has 25,000 pairs) have few predators, and the chief destroyers of eggs and chicks appear to be other gulls. The parents defend their own territories and nests with vigor, but they cannot be everywhere at once, and when the chicks begin to wander they suffer heavy losses from their neighbors. In Paynter's study the eggs suffered 29 per cent mortality during the incubation period of 25 days; the chicks lost half their number before fledging at an average of 45 days from hatching; but the surviving adults may live to great ages, perhaps to 25 years in significant numbers, and die at an average rate of about 15 per cent per year.

Studies of clutch and brood size in birds have pointed up in a particularly neat fashion the great difference between fecundity and natality (as the ecologist uses those terms — fecundity meaning the number of eggs that hatch, the *fertility rate* of the demographer, while natality means successful reproduction). The gull data imply that the over-all form of the survivorship curve is J-shaped, the heaviest mortality falling on the young of pre-reproductive ages. Plainly (although there are no exact data) the form for a species like the oyster or a pelagic fish is even more J-shaped, whereas not all birds give quite so steep J-shapes as does the gull: for passerine birds that build protected nests, especially in nest boxes, typical hatching rates are above 80 per cent, and fledging rates are also typically 80 per cent, so that the proportion of fledged young from complete clutches averages 67 per cent in hole-nesting species. Now the average number of eggs laid by a bird is somewhat variable within the species, with environmental, hereditary, and psychologic factors all playing complicated roles. In some species, such as the Great Tit, it has been found that the number of eggs laid is slightly lower at higher population densities. But birds are not like Daphnia, grossly susceptible to environmental influence on fecundity, and the variability in fecundity is not nearly enough to account for the variable rates at which the populations increase according to circumstances. What varies much more systematically is the proportion of survival to fledging, i.e. the net natality is heavily influenced by mortality of the young. And this in turn not only varies with the clutch size but does so in remarkably different ways.

In the herring gull the proportion of eggs that hatched from three-egg nests was 80.4 per cent, from two-egg nests it was 56.4 per cent, and in one-egg nests it was only 28.6 per cent. Paynter supposed that incomplete clutches, or those from which one or two eggs are lost quite early, do not provide adequate psychic stimulus to persuade the parents to guard them. But after the eggs hatch there is no difference in chick survival according to the clutch size; the parents usually bring more than enough food for three chicks in one meal. The mechanism is quite otherwise in the alpine swift, which is dependent on good weather for catching flying insects, food for the young often being in critically short supply. Here there is no difference in hatching according to clutch size, because the nests are well protected from predators, but the proportion of young that fledge from one-, two-, three-, and four-egg clutches is 97, 87, 79, and 60 per cent respectively. In consequence the loss of young at the largest clutch size balances the gain provided by an extra egg, and the most efficient clutch size for parents to have is set at three. Lack maintains that the reason the two-egg layers have not been entirely replaced by three-egg layers is that there is a balanced form of genetic polymorphism, comparable to the case of human sickle-cell anemia, (in which the heterozygotes are more immune to malaria and so are at a selective advantage over people who lack the gene entirely). Heterozygosis for clutch size in swifts would be favored by the year-to-year variability of weather, the two-egg layers being at a selective advantage in some years and in some localities.

But still another type of relation exists in passerine birds. In the starling Lack finds that there is no advantage of small clutches (of one, two, three, or four) in respect to fledging, and the average number raised per brood continues to increase, at least in Dutch starlings, from five- to six- to seven- to eight-egg clutches. But the more young that fledge the lower their average weight, and the less well equipped they are to survive the fearful days after they leave the nest. So the proportion that survive at least three months after fledging proves to be markedly greater for the birds that started life in smaller clutches; the mortality that falls on larger clutches of swifts is deferred, in the starling, until after the nestlings leave.

These three examples not only show how complex are the factors governing population equilibria in nature; they direct attention to the critical importance of juvenile survival. Parental care is minimal in marine invertebrates and fishes; clouds of eggs and sperm cost little metabolically, and presumably a sessile species like the oyster gains enough advantage from the pelagic dispersal of its larvae to offset the colossal loss of gametes, larvae, and spat. But such a reproductive system, though possible for higher plants, is altogether too wasteful to be practiced by a mammal. The price that mammals have paid for being both terrestrial and successful includes the expense of elaborate devices to protect the embryos from loss of water, and these devices are designed for high efficiency, not for high productivity. So we do not expect to find mammalian survivorship so markedly J-shaped as is that of an oyster, or even of a gull. Moreover, although the advantage conferred by ability to learn does not show up in wild birds' patterns of mortality, perhaps it will show up in those of mammals.

The available studies confirm both deductions, the latter with more certainty than the former, owing to various difficulties in the collection of evidence on young animals in the wild. For example many life tables have been computed from skeletons, found fossil or merely picked up on the range, the age at death being estimated from growth rings on horns or from less reliable criteria. The data are then reasonably satisfactory for adults, but the fragile skeletons of the young are underrepresented in the sample. Fortunately we usually know or can guess at the reproduction rate of a mammal species, so the loss of young before they enter our sample can be estimated. Guesses approximating 70 per cent mortality between birth and maturity have been made for several large ungulates, living and extinct, by Kurtén; if we add to this an adult mortality approximating 30 per cent per year in middle life the result is a curve that dips sharply in the youngest ages, but not nearly so sharply as does that of the herring gull. Again, the adult mortality of snowshoe hares in Minnesota was very constant at 70 per cent per year, but the mortality of the young of the year varied from a maximum of 92 per cent to a minimum of 8 per cent. Since some modern human populations, India's for example, suffer 55 per cent mortality between birth and maturity, we can say that juvenile mortality of wild mammals, though heavier than that of adults, is not necessarily more severe than that of civilized man.

It is even more interesting to find that mammalian mortality rates decrease with age and experience, so that the survivorship curves, from maturity onward to old age, are convex upward exactly like that of man. When I first found this for the Dall mountain sheep of Mt. McKinley I thought it might be an artifact, but the fact has been abundantly confirmed for other ungulates, including several deer, several extinct muskoxen, the chamois, and the woolly mammoth, and for one carnivore, the hyaenid Ictitherium.

The Dall sheep has a single important predator, the timber wolf. Death by predation can be avoided by at least two kinds of activity: group defense of the young by a circle of horned heads (a trick shared by the modern muskox, among others), and systematic flight to altitudes so high that wolves cannot pursue. Both kinds of behavior are presumably learned, i.e. they are the kinds of behavior that prove to be learned in domestic sheep, and they are learned by communication in a social context; they therefore are indistinguishable from *culture*. Analogous but probably not identical traits of behavior presumably underlie the notable survival of the deer and other large mammals.

Cultural transmission of learned behavior in nonhuman mammals has been most convincingly demonstrated in a social rodent, the prairie dog. King has shown that the social unit, or coterie, not all of whose members are related by blood, defends its common territory against members of other coteries. The boundaries of the territory are arbitrary, and have to be learned, yet they may remain stable while the personnel of the groups undergoes complete turnover. This astonishing discovery should make almost anyone take a heightened interest in rodents, and since much is known about rodent population dynamics, natality in particular, I make no apology for the mousy nature of my next topic.

AGGRESSION, ANXIETY, AND NATALITY

House mice live wild in many parts of the world, having been spread by man from their ancestral home on the steppes of Russia. Even in northern countries, like Great Britain, they may live wild throughout the year, competing with and sometimes displacing the native rodents; as opportunity arises they display their superior ability to become commensal with man, the ability that brought them to such countries in the first place. As wild animals they are distinguished by what is probably the smallest home range of any rodent; in one study on Guam the maximum distance over which mice moved for many weeks was 36 yards for males, 30 yards for females. In barns near Baltimore, Brown found that 98 per cent of the population moved less than 16 yards between successive points of capture. When the environment is three-dimensional, like the standing ricks of unthreshed wheat of Laurie's British study, densities can vary from less than two to nearly fourteen mice per cubic meter. In an elaborate study of the utilization of space by mice Calhoun found that the probability of their stopping in un-structured space is very small; when highly motivated, as in the search for shelter or nesting material, mice quickly learn to select the shortest route to a goal.

These facts imply a low degree of dispersal from a desired habitat, and intense competition for goals within one; mice habitually live close to other mice, but "of all their wives' relations they like themselves the best" — if threatened, they would rather stay and fight than run away. Moreover, as in all other vertebrates when crowded, a dominance hier-archy (called "peck order" in flocks of chickens) is readily established as a consequence of experience of fighting, so that mice respond to each other as individuals; but their individual lives are short as well as brut-ish, and upward social mobility poses a constant threat to the status of the higher ranking individuals.

Laurie studied British mice in four distinct environments: the ordi-nary urban one in the back streets of Oxford, a cold-storage plant, a flour depot, and the country habitat of ricks and cornfields. Judged by the incidence of pregnancy and the annual litter production, the four environments were increasingly favorable in that order: urban, cold-storage plant, flour depot, and ricks. The number of embryos per preg-nant female averaged higher in the cold-storage plant, but the average age at maturity was delayed there; the surprising thing is that mice can live there at all, let alone breed all year around, in constant darkness at 15 degrees Fahrenheit, and on a high-protein diet. The number of daughters born per pregnant female per year was 16 in the urban habitat, 23 in the cold-storage plant, 25 in the flour depot, and 32 in the ricks. We can conclude that the country mouse has it all over the city mouse; urbanization, for mice as well as men, brings social problems and declining fertility.

At least it brings declining fertility; that it brings social problems I can best demonstrate by describing some laboratory studies. Strecker established mouse populations in a junkroom in the basement of a build-ing at the University of Wisconsin, fed them on controlled amounts of food, and set traps in the neighboring offices and laboratories. When the food was limited to 250 grams per day, the population grew slowly but regularly until its food consumption leveled off at 250 grams per day. While the mice were increasing they saw no reason to leave home, but when the food supply became limiting the surplus mice began to leave the room in trickles, and then in droves. Next, Strecker and Emlen set up populations in two large pens from which escape was impossible, and fed them 250 grams of food per day. Each population increased in time to a peak, but the larger initial population increased to a very high peak of more than 100 mice, whereupon reproduction stopped abruptly, the gonads of the adult females regressed, and the population declined to the original level. The smaller initial population increased to about 40, declined to 30, and rose again to 40; reproduction was more or less normal at all times.

The question that arises is, why should one population level off at 40 when another goes on to reach more than 100? Southwick's studies confirm this remarkable variability, and also give us some insight into its causes. Aware that the social structure of the pens might have some bearing on the kinetics, Southwick set up three identical populations in pens with concentrated areas of shelter, food, and water, and another three in pens where the essential needs of mice were spatially dispersed. At first sight the results seem puzzling and inconclusive: the maximum population sizes reached in the three concentrated pens were 131, 127, and 25, and in the dispersed pens they were 81, 138, and 59. The averages are the same, but the enormous variability makes them meaningless. Moreover, all the populations stopped growing at the end of their second summer, regardless of the density and of the fact that food was always abundant.

Closer observation shows that the social structure varied enough to explain the variable results, but did so in unpredictable ways, being unrelated to the geometric structure of the feeding and nesting arrangements. In four of the populations the live birth rate declined as a consequence of crowding. But in two of these there was a suppression of ovulation and spermatogenesis, apparently associated with poor condition and inadequate diet — there was plenty of food, but a few highly aggressive males kept the other mice from feeding. In two other pens where the birth rate fell the mice were adequately fed and fully fertile; but here the social structure was highly unstable with much fighting, and the pregnancy rate was low, apparently because the males fought so hard over the females that few of them mated successfully. In a fifth pen the birth rate remained unchanged with crowding, but the survival of litters was seriously affected, as it was in all the other pens. In the sixth pen, which never supported more than 25 mice, a few dominant but impotent males were able to suppress all reproduction until they died.

The one consistent result that emerges is that successful reproduction, and especially the survival of litters, is sharply inhibited by fighting; litter mortality was greatest when the observed number of fights exceeded one per mouse per hour. But whereas most of the fights are initiated by males, the psychology of the females is equally affected; cannibalism and desertion are the chief causes of loss of litters, but underlying these forms of behavior is the failure of maternal drive. If nests are well constructed, i.e. covered or of bowl shape, they are also well defended, and 60 to 90 per cent of the litters survive to weaning; in platform-shaped nests the survival is much lower, especially if more than two females occupy the same nest; and litters that were not cared for in nests did not survive at all.

The importance of social status in reproduction was dramatically shown in rats by an experiment of Calhoun. Food and water were provided in a central space, but nesting opportunity was so arranged as to produce central and peripheral sub-populations. A dominance hierarchy was established, with the central rats taking priority in feeding. The central rats had larger numbers of successful litters than did the peripheral rats, though the incidence of pregnancy was the same in both. Because of the reduction of food, the peripheral rats grew more slowly. And, because weight is the deciding factor in fighting, the peripheral rats were maintained in permanently low social status as long as the study lasted.

Now fighting is a learned response in rats and mice; Scott's work suggests that frustration leads to aggression only so long as aggression provides a satisfactory solution, i.e. is rewarding. And King found that there as a critical period, between twenty and thirty days of age in a mouse, in which fighting is either learned or is not, according to its reward value. Play and social contact normally teach a young mouse to fight during the socialization process. Fighting, then, is apparently a cultural trait. Evidently this is the explanation for the relative unpredictability of population responses in Southwick's experiments.

Once learned, however, intense fighting has some predictable consequences for natality. The guiding principle here is Selye's "General Adaptation Syndrome" (GAS), a suite of largely endocrine responses to various forms of shock or stress, in which the adrenal cortex plays a central role. According to Selye's massively documented theory, the reaction to stress is first given by the pituitary gland, which secretes adrenocorticotropic hormone (ACTH). The adrenal hormones then mobilize the resources of the body to resist — the blood sugar increases to provide ready energy for flight or tension, the kidney becomes an endocrine gland, with resulting effects on salt and protein balance, etc. Under conditions of chronic stress the adrenal cortex is hypertrophied, and its hyperactivity inhibits the production of other pituitary hormones, notably the gonadotropins, for reproduction is a luxury when stress is severe and chronic. Increased stress may then cause death from "shock," the resources of the body already being mobilized to the full; the proximate cause of death is hypoglycemia, or lack of sufficient sugar in the blood. Selye maintains that anxiety is a form of stress, and when chronic decreases resistance to other stresses. There is no doubt that anxiety is communicable, in mice as well as men, and so we see again the essential kinship between man and the vertebrates.

The view that Selye's GAS plays a major role in the population dynamics of mammals is exceedingly persuasive. Christian has found that crowding of mice leads to hypertrophy of the adrenal cortex, along with the ramifying effects that Selye predicts: delayed puberty, delayed involution of the thymus, regression of secondary sex characters, and depression of fecundity; the weight of the adrenal glands in Christian's mice was a direct function of the population size. Similar results were obtained with crowded meadow voles by Louch, who lays special emphasis on reduced production of prolactin as the probable proximate cause of reduced maternal drive. Clarke and Chitty are finding the same kinds of endocrine responses in British voles. And the notion that shock disease is a consequence of excessive density, and therefore of excessive stress by fighting, is well supported by the studies of the snowshoe hare. The peak of the population cycle is followed by a crash; seemingly healthy hares may die when trapped or when merely chased, and elaborate studies of the incidence of disease show no obvious reason for the mortality other than hypoglycemia.

So we are beginning at last to glimpse the mechanisms of the remarkable cyclic fluctuations in animal abundance. The three- or four-year cycle of mice, voles, and lemmings, and the ten-year cycle of snowshoe hares — the latter clearly reflected in the ten-year cycle of lynx fur returns to the Hudson's Bay Company — are evidently not related to

83

sunspot numbers, to weather, or, necessarily, to varying supplies of food. They seem to be generated internally by psychic and endocrine responses to population density. There is even some reason to suspect that the mechanism works both ways from equilibrium; that is, there may be an optimum density for natality in voles. Chitty suggests that a moderate amount of strife enhances the litter size over that of isolated control pairs, but the data supporting this statement are unpublished as yet. True or not, no great importance need be attached to it, for uncrowded voles are fully capable of repopulating a suitable environment. As Ray remarked of the lemming, "Nature had not been such a niggard of her gifts" as to require a special stimulus for breeding.

The experimental studies, with their cannibalism and other deranged behavior, their "shock disease," and their heartless records of "one fight per mouse per hour," probably emphasize unduly what Malthus called the positive checks to increase — pestilence and warfare. The situations are of course abnormal. Still, field ecologists have long known that periodic disturbances of equilibrium are the rule, and have devoted much fruitless effort to the search for extrinsic causes. Are these fluctuations to be expected in animals that have culture but no ethics? Are they part of the price the mammals pay for being, successfully, sentient, thinking, social beings like ourselves? Or are they, perhaps, fundamentally adaptive? These questions bring us back to the top of the tower, for a final consideration of statics, this time in terms of numbers instead of masses and productivities.

OSCILLATING EQUILIBRIA

Ten years ago, when Hutchinson and I wanted to make the point that an animal population can fluctuate regularly for reasons intrinsic to the system, the foregoing facts about small mammals were undiscovered, and we were forced to rely on the case of Daphnia. To return to Daphnia now is something of an anticlimax, because while it is still true that Daphnia populations oscillate without external cause, Daphnia is so unlike a vertebrate biologically that its relevance to the classic cycles is remote. Nevertheless it is useful in constructing a mathematical model of population equilibrium to think in terms of this delightfully simple and prolific animal.

What draws our attention is the delayed reaction, first clearly shown by Pratt, between population density and the attainment of appropriate birth and death rates. Certainly, as numbers increase, the birth rate slows down and the death rate rises, but each reaction takes a little time. On the rising curve of population growth most of the animals have spent most of their lives at lower densities, and they reproduce too rapidly for the conditions of the moment — so the numbers overshoot equilibrium. Then, with births minimal and deaths maximal, the population declines; but now most of the animals have spent most of their lives at higher densities, and they die too rapidly for conditions of the moment. Undershooting is the result, and so the oscillation continues, though in time it progressively diminishes — is "damped off." The system is analogous to complicated electronic control systems, and engineers would say the population "hunts" — like the lid on a pan of boiling water.

Electrical engineers get interested when biologists talk about damped oscillations; "jitter" is sometimes deliberately built into a mechanical control system, for instance to do away with the necessity for overcoming friction in moving from one state to another. An appropriate equation for the corresponding growth process starts with the logistic equation (see above):

$$\frac{dN}{dt} = bN\left(\frac{K-N}{K}\right)$$

Two kinds of time lag can be allowed to start with: the time needed for an animal to start reproduction when conditions are favorable, and the time required for the individuals to react to changing density by altering their birth and death rates. Letting these time lags be $t - t_1$ and $t - t_2$ respectively, Wangersky and Cunningham give:

$$\frac{dN(t)}{dt} = bN_{(t-t_1)} \frac{K-N_{(t-t_2)}}{K}$$

Such equations rapidly become intractable, but they can be studied with profit by use of an analogue computer of modest design. They are much easier to study in this way, in fact, than to provide with empirical data from real populations, yet in principle all constants and variables in such equations can be evaluated experimentally. By assuming reasonable values for birth rates, equilibrium densities, and time lags it is a simple matter to test out whether the resulting population oscillates indefinitely, shows damped oscillations, or approaches saturation in the orthodox way. The same procedure can be used to study interaction

85

between two populations, whether in a predator-prey or a competition situation, but these situations, if realistically formulated, exceed the present capacity of the Yale computer. What emerges from this admittedly abstract approach is, first, that almost anything that populations have ever been observed to do can be duplicated by the computer, and second, that damped oscillations should be more frequent than any other kind of equilibrium.

This last appears to be a conclusion of first-rate importance. Its basis is probably twofold: a species that approaches equilibrium slowly and steadily in the classic way supposed by Pearl and other early students is insufficiently reactive to take advantage of changing environments, whether they change seasonally or randomly. But to generate an infinite series of oscillations requires very careful balance of birth rates and time lags, and if the amplitude of the oscillations is great the chances are good that one of them will take the population too close to zero. Real animals, unlike mathematical ones, cannot take fractional values and still recover their numbers; an oscillating population is particularly vulnerable to disturbances. What seems to be built into living systems, then, is an adaptive ability to undergo damped oscillations.

Has all this any relevance for demography? I think it has. Man's power of increase, though low for an animal, is adequate to produce great changes in the lifetimes of individual members. So the time lags, though also very long, are finite. A certain amount of overshooting would not be fatal, and might even be salutary, as well as biologically inevitable. The hope, and the challenge, lie in the fact that the world is now more unified than it used to be. So long as a tribal unit is free to think of itself as independent, reserving the name of "people" for itself, the Micmac's loss may be the Cherokee's gain, at least in respect to productivity of human substance, and the total extinction of one tribe may not loom large in the scheme of things. But now what happens in Timbuktu affects us all, and the equilibrium that I think is near, whatever form it takes, will apply to the whole world. Self-regulation of numbers may be nearer than we are accustomed to thinking, and one can expect that the process will in the long run be less painful than it is for mice, or even for Daphnia. But my white carven tower now begins to look like a soapbox.

The Genetic Future of Man

IN COMMON with all other living species, both plant and animal, man is subject to the laws of heredity and to the influence of his environment. Modern man is the result of slow evolutionary development during the past million years, based upon variation, natural selection, and survival of the fittest. Man is still a variable species and has potential capacities for further development or for regression and decay. To a great extent modern man has so controlled his environment that the ancient types of natural selection now play little part in survival and reproduction. But he has not controlled his heredity as he has controlled the heredity of his cultivated plants and his domesticated animals. Most of our crop plants and farm animals would probably not survive in nature, but in a controlled environment they far surpass their wild ancestors in their economic value.

We have a heritage of genetic traits based largely upon survival in a primitive society, where the criteria for natural selection were based upon the escape from early death. Physical strength and endurance were necessary for survival in a hostile and competitive world. Natural immunity to disease increased the chances for survival. Intelligence and foresight were needed to avoid natural enemies and to provide for the future. Love and compassion were also of great importance in caring for the children, the family, and the members of the community. But with limited control of nature, and no control of disease, death rates were very high. Only women of high fecundity could produce enough children to ensure the survival of the race.

The heritage of high fertility in an era of low death rates has led to the recent explosive growth of the world's population. During most of man's existence high death rates demanded high birth rates, but population growth could not have exceeded an average of .03 or .04 per cent annually. Before the advent of agriculture the world population could hardly have exceeded 20 million. Agriculture provided more food and population increased, but at the beginning of the Christian era the world population probably did not exceed a third of a billion with a growth rate of less than 0.1 per cent annually. Population continued to grow but did not reach a billion until early in the nineteenth century. Explosive population growth began only with the advent of modern medicine less than a hundred years ago. During the last half of the nineteenth century the population growth rate was about 0.7 per cent and the world's people numbered little more than 1,600 million. Today the world population is about 2,700 million and is growing at a rate of about 1.5 per cent annually. At this rate the population of the world would exceed 5 billion by the end of this century. But this rate is far from the possible maximum and in some countries primitive birth rates, with low death rates, have resulted in growth rates of about 3 per cent per year.

Growth rates of even 1 per cent per year cannot long be maintained; the inevitable result must be starvation and an increase in the death rate. Agriculture cannot possibly keep pace, for any significant period of time, with the population growth resulting from uncontrolled birth rates and controlled death rates. Modern public health services can reduce death rates to low levels even in countries where the people live little above subsistence levels. But unless population growth in all parts of the world can be reduced by lower birth rates man can look forward to renewed high death rates, poverty, and strife. The innate fecundity of primitive man, which was essential for the survival of the species, is now the greatest threat to modern civilization.

Following industrialization in the Western nations birth rates were reduced to little more than replacement levels and the means of subsistence and the standards of living have increased much more rapidly than have populations. But these countries have faced another problem — differential birth rates. In these countries those who were most able to provide the necessary food, shelter, education, and medical care had fewer children while those with little education and the lowest income had the largest families. In the depression years of the 1930s the only group of urban couples in the United States who had birth rates sufficient to increase their numbers were those on relief, while college graduates produced little more than half the children required for replacement of this group. If poverty and ignorance are associated with defective heredity such differential birth rates could result in a race of mental and physical defectives. If poverty and ignorance are largely associated with an unfavorable environment, children raised in an environment of social irresponsibility would tend to be similarly irresponsible. Both heredity and environment are involved in irresponsible reproduction, but the environmental factor can be more easily controlled than can the genetic factors.

There is some evidence that the differential birth rate may be a transient phase in the demographic development of a country. In Sweden, and to a lesser extent in some other countries, birth rates of the various socioeconomic groups are becoming more uniform. Such results would be expected as educational and economic opportunities are improved. But with greater equality of opportunity and an improved environment, the remaining irresponsible parenthood is likely to be largely associated with genetic defects — leading to permanent deleterious consequences.

Natural selection, in conjunction with high death rates, has not eliminated low fecundity, physical defects, and mental aberrations and deficiencies. In the people of European ancestry about 10 per cent of the married couples are sterile or can produce only one or two children. According to Tage Kemp, director of the Institute of Human Genetics in Denmark, between 2 and 3 per cent of the people of European ancestry are seriously impaired by mental or physical defects of genetic origin; Jan Böök, director of Sweden's State Institute of Human Genetics, estimates the incidence is considerably higher. Most of these defectives are the feeble-minded and insane, but the congenital cripples, deaf, and blind are numerous.

It is possible that the weakening of natural selection during the past few hundred years has increased the incidence of deleterious genetic traits in populations of European ancestry, although these deleterious genes were present in our earlier ancestors. They were carried in the heterozygous state only to appear in later generations, while occasional new mutations added to our genetic burden. Moreover in a primitive agricultural culture some degree of mental deficiency was no great handicap in survival and reproduction. In any case we do carry a load of mutations which are deleterious to the individual and to society in a modern world.

Some of these deleterious genetic traits need no longer be a major handicap in the survival of the individual. Clubfoot can be remedied by surgery, the effects of diabetes can be controlled by insulin, certain forms of anemia can be controlled by vitamins, poor vision can be remedied by glasses and poor hearing by hearing aids. The mentally subnormal can often be trained to do routine work, and the mentally ill can often be helped by psychiatrists to return to normal life.

Even deleterious genes may have a selective advantage under certain conditions. The sickle cell gene is a striking illustration of a genetic condition which is highly deleterious in the homozygous condition, yet survives at a high frequency in malarious areas of Africa, Italy, Greece, Turkey, and India. Allison has shown that in some Negro tribes in Africa the gene is carried by about 40 per cent of the population and that 4 per cent receive both recessive genes from their parents. Most of the homozygous segregates die in childhood from sickle cell anemia and only comparatively few survive to reproduce. Yet the gene persists at a high level in spite of the fact that about a sixth of the sickle cell genes are lost from the population each generation.

The brilliant work of Allison has shown that the sickle cell gene persists because it confers considerable immunity to malarial infection. He has shown that the frequency of the sickle cell gene is higher in areas where malaria is most prevalent. The protective effect of the gene, even in the heterozyous condition, has more than offset the lethal effect in the homozygous condition. Allison predicts that the gene frequency would decline if the African tribes were relatively free from malaria. This prediction was substantiated by his study of American Negroes. He estimates that the frequency of the gene was more than 22 per cent in the Negro population brought to the United States some 250–300 years ago. Crossing with Indians and whites may have reduced the frequency to about 15 per cent, but the frequency among American Negroes is now only about 9 per cent. In a malaria-free environment the gene no longer had a selective advantage and the lethal effect in homozygous carriers greatly reduced the gene frequency in about ten generations. The frequency will continue to decrease. This is an exceptional case, but it is possible that other genes may be subject to environmental conditions in a similar manner.

The continued control of the environment can be expected to increase the frequency of deleterious genes in a population, but it may also increase the frequency of hereditary traits better adapted to a complex and regimented society. We have seen how our domesticated animals have been greatly modified by controlled breeding and selection in a relatively short time.

It has been shown by Walker Dawson that wildness or tameness in mice is an inherited trait and that wildness is the dominant character. In the second generation the frequency of the two types indicated a multiple factor mechanism of heredity. In tame and wild rats David Davis found that tameness was associated with a decrease in the size and function of the adrenal gland. The decrease in adrenalin secretion resulted in more docile individuals. These genetically tame individuals were able to survive only in an environment of security. Is there any possibility that the "domestication" of man could lead to similar results in a society of material security?

In the Communist-dominated countries those who deviate from the party line are likely to be liquidated permanently or sent to labor camps for long periods of time. Over many generations negative selection might decrease the frequency of "wild" genes responsible for nonconformity and original thought. In the free world social pressures are also likely to lead to regimentation and conformity with the increasing complexity of social and economical life. Even in this country no government employee and few deans of medical colleges would dare, at least publicly, to advocate birth control as a part of a public health program. Few social workers would risk their jobs by suggesting that some of the "underprivileged" are suffering from bad heredity. At present the intellectual rebel is not likely to be liquidated in our country. Although social pressures for regimented conformity are increasing, it is highly improbable that either artificial selection or social pressures will lead to genetic domestication of the human race. Man is essentially a wild animal and is likely to remain so. More social conformity may be necessary in our complex civilization but it can be attained by education and understanding.

Among the deleterious genetic changes that may be ascribed to control of our environment, the survival of the genetically handicapped is only one of the factors involved. The problem of greatest concern at the moment is the increased mutation rate resulting from use of atomic energy in peace or war. Even if atomic energy is not developed for military purposes, its use in industry is inevitable. The world's reserves of oil could well be far from adequate before the end of this century if demands continue at the present rate. If all the world is to be industrialized the reserves of coal would be depleted in a few hundred years. Our industrial culture cannot long continue without new sources of abundant energy and atomic energy appears to be much more promising than the harnessing of solar energy.

The industrial use of atomic energy could be a genetic hazard. It is known that the ionizing produced in the generation of atomic energy will cause mutations and chromosome aberrations. The production of gene mutations is dependent on the total radiation dose regardless of its intensity. Very low exposures over long periods of time can produce as many mutations as the same dose given in a few minutes. The frequency of chromosomal aberrations, however, is dependent upon dosage intensity and an exposure of 200 roentgens in a few minutes is much more effective than an exposure of 200 roentgens over a period of several days or weeks. A single short exposure of about 450 roentgens is lethal to man. The same dose accumulated over a period of several years would not be immediately fatal, but it would reduce life expectancy considerably, and increase the spontaneous mutation rate at least several fold.

How much radiation could the human race tolerate without excessively shortening the span of life or without increasing the mutation rate to excessive levels? It is true that any increase in the exposure to ionizing radiation is deleterious and will increase the mutation rate. The recent increase in radioactivity due to atomic bomb tests is probably of little significance so far as new mutations are concerned. Curt Stern has estimated that the exposure of our population to 0.1 roentgens might produce sufficient mutations to result in perhaps 150 defective progeny among 4 million births. Any increase of defectives is of course unfortunate, but considering that the heritage of spontaneous mutations results in at least 40,000 defective births each year the additional defectives from radiation at present levels would be statistically of little significance.

Even the survivors of the Hiroshima and Nagasaki atomic bombs do not appear to have accumulated a dangerous load of new deleterious mutations though the average survivor received perhaps 20 roentgens of ionizing radiation. The incidence of abnormal births among the survivors does not appear to have increased above the level of the population that was not exposed. However, most of the recessive mutations which may have been produced will not be expressed for many generations.

The spontaneous mutation rate is estimated by Curt Stern to produce as many as two abnormal births per thousand, or 0.2 per cent. Although the natural or background radiation is about 3 or 4 roentgens per human generation it is improbable that natural radiation is responsible for more than a small fraction of the spontaneous mutations. But substantial increases in radiation will increase the mutation rate. A committee appointed by the National Academy of Science has estimated that the present mutation rate might be doubled by exposure of the population to 5–150 roentgens over the first thirty years of life. The best estimates by competent geneticists range from 30 to 80 roentgens. The doubling of the present mutation rate would be a heavy burden, but much greater increases might become intolerable.

It is inevitable that some increase in the mutation rate will result from the industrial use of atomic energy. Even with the utmost care accidents will happen. Intensive exposures of 450 roentgens or more will be lethal and exposure to lower levels of radiation will shorten the life span and induce mutations. Most of these mutations will be deleterious and most of them will be recessive. The few dominant lethal mutations will be automatically eliminated, but dominant nonlethal genes can be transmitted to future generations if not eliminated by natural or controlled selection. The great majority of the induced mutations will be recessives and will not usually result in abnormalities unless both mutated genes are passed on to the same person. In some cases the presence of the two mutated genes in the homozygous condition may be modified by other factors, either hereditary or environmental. The presence of a single mutated gene will not ordinarily be detected and will have little or no deleterious effect. Many people will carry the mutated gene in the heterozygous state. As the mutation increases in frequency the chances of both genes coming together in a single person are increased. If for example the gene is present in the heterozygous condition with a frequency of 1 in 500 persons, only 1 in a million will be homozygous. But if the gene frequency is high and 1 in 16 are carriers, 1 per 1,000 can be expected to suffer from the double dose of the deleterious recessive gene. Lethal or highly deleterious dominant genes would soon be eliminated, but recessive genes could be carried at low frequencies and rarely appear. An increase in the mutation rate or the selective advantage of the heterozygote would increase the gene frequency until it reached an equilibrium with its lethal effects in the homozygous condition.

If most deleterious mutations resulted in gametic sterility or early embryonic death, modern man could tolerate many times the present mutation rate because his inherent fertility is several times that necessary to ensure adequate population growth in a modern society with low death rates. Unfortunately most of the deleterious mutations result in mental and physical disabilities which are a serious burden to the individual and to society. Böök reports that in Sweden the approximate frequency of genetic, or supposedly genetic, diseases and defects is 1 per 1,000 for congenital clubfoot, 1 per 300 for convulsive disorders, 1 per 200 for diabetes, 1 per 100 for imbecility or feeble-mindedness, 1 per 100 for manic-depressive psychosis, and more than 1 per 100 for schizophrenia. He concludes that these and other "*severe* genetic diseases and defects disable some 5 to 10 per cent of the Western populations." He finds that while infections and parasitic diseases as the cause of death decreased 73 per cent in Sweden between 1936–40 and 1951, mental diseases and congenital abnormalities increased about 50 per cent.

One of our leading psychiatrists, William Menninger, estimates that in the United States at least 10 per cent of the people are suffering from occasional or chronic mental illness. They include 30 per cent of the patients in our general hospitals, the 4 million cases of problem drinking, many of those who each year commit nearly 2 million crimes, and many of the half million or more juvenile delinquents. Environmental factors of home and social conditions play an important part in mental illness as well as inherent mental deficiencies. But genetic abnormalities of mind and body are a major problem of our modern civilization, where natural selection no longer operates in the traditional fashion.

As Muller has emphasized, the consequences of modern agricultural, industrial, and medical science deserve at least as much attention as do the hazards of nuclear energy. He believes that the avoidance of natural selection will probably add more mutation in the next eight generations than would the exposure of every American now alive to the

94

amount of radiation received by the average Hiroshima survivor. In commenting on the control of death from genetic mental and physical defects he concludes: "The saving of a life does not automatically justify its production of offspring, for the chief criterion on which to base decisions in the planning of parenthood would be the welfare of the descendants themselves."

As I now see it, the most urgent need is the artificial control of the birth rate to little more than replacement levels in all parts of the world. We have inherited from our primitive ancestors a degree of fecundity far in excess of the needs of modern man. Uncontrolled fecundity, as I have indicated, can lead only to starvation, poverty, and high death rates, regardless of any considerable advances in agriculture or the production of synthetic food. If, for example, the people of Massachusetts, where we are told by some that "birth control is against God's Law," maintained the birth rates prevalent in 1800 and the death rates of 1950, the present population of about 5 million would in 100 years equal the present population of the entire country; in 200 years it would approach the present population of the world, and in 500 years there would be only standing room on the land surface of the earth. The artificial control of the death rate makes necessary a comparable control of the birth rate if our modern civilization is to be maintained.

The second greatest need is the prevention of an increase in the frequency of deleterious genes inherited from past generations. The least we can do is to try to prevent reproduction by those who are suffering from serious mental and physical disabilities of genetic origin. Considerable progress can be made by educational programs. The greatest immediate need is for more genetic information in the medical schools, as a foundation of a broader program for the general public. No responsible person would deliberately burden his family and society with physical and mental cripples. More direct methods may have to be used among the more irresponsible prospective parents, but if the state must undertake the care and protection of the mental defectives, the feeble-minded, and the chronic criminals, it should have some authority to control their reproduction as well as the other forms of their behavior that it already controls.

The elimination of reproduction by the mental and physical defectives would not of course eliminate the deleterious genes from the population since most of the defectives are produced by normal persons carrying the defective genes in a heterozygous condition. Although it is now possible to identify some of these deleterious genes in the heterozygous state the complete analysis of all prospective parents is not yet justified. Much more research must be done on the genetic nature of many physical and mental defects and on the role of environmental and medical factors in their control. But a program of "negative eugenics" could do much to alleviate the unnecessary burden resulting from irresponsible reproduction by those who are already a burden to society and to themselves. Eventually a program of positive eugenics will have sufficient scientific foundation to be justified.

Deleterious genes inherited from our ancestors cannot be eliminated, but their frequency could be reduced even though spontaneous new mutations will continue to be produced. If, however, the mutation rate is substantially increased any progress made by eugenic controls might be offset by new deleterious mutations. We will have to live in an atomic age, but we do not yet know what the hazards may be. Much work is being done on the induction of mutations by radiation at Oak Ridge and elsewhere, and these results should be of value in determining more accurately the hazards of ionizing radiation. It seems highly improbable that the industrial use of atomic energy would ever equal the immediate toll of death and injury now caused by automobiles, but the effects on future generations could be more serious. We do know that ionizing radiation can increase the mutation rate and every effort should be made to prevent any unnecessary exposure to this mutagenic agent.

If man is unwilling to let the forces of nature and natural selection shape the course of human evolution he must accept this responsibility. Since we are not very well prepared to assume this responsibility, the problems of man's future must be approached with humility and tolerance. But there are some problems which need immediate attention. No rational person can deny that there can be no permanent control of the death rate unless the birth rate is also controlled, and the desire to postpone death is almost universal. No humane person would advocate the deliberate production of the mentally and physically deformed who are a burden to society and to themselves. The least we can do is to try to remedy these conditions by social and medical therapy and to reduce the incidence of their reproduction.

Since the environment is a major factor in evolution, and particularly in the social evolution of man, the social environment must be improved. Modern man has inherited not only his burden of deleterious genes, but also many superstitions and taboos which are not conducive to rational thought and understanding in a modern world. It is not enough that man be freed from starvation and disease; he must also be freed from ancient creeds and dogma which are so prevalent in the world today.

Cultural Aspects of the Population Problem

IT IS impossible to consider the various problems of population, however much they may at base reside in biology, without reference to culture. Man differs from other forms of animal life in having created, outside of the biological context, that series of common understandings — those fundamental definitions of himself — which are ringed about by tradition and established custom and which are called culture.

The human being cannot be regarded as a creature of instinct; his behavior is learned. This being so, the various societies of men have fashioned various systems of value and conceptual being which come to touch every aspect of human existence. Why there should be differences among the various socio-cultural groups of mankind, different value systems, great variability in outlook, remarkable diversity in institution and concept, need not be of primary concern here. This is a historical problem, an ecological and an environmental problem, but never a biological one.

That these differences do exist, however, and do affect our relations with one another, we must recognize. Indeed, this symposium to treat the subject of population is one reflection of an interest in a problem which has its roots in western European tradition and civilization. In Western culture the "population problem" is rooted in the Judaeo-Christian background which places an intrinsic worth on the human being and on human life. Not that human life lacks value in other cultures, but it must be recognized that the ways in which this concept is viewed differ markedly from one human society to another. Further, if our concern is with a "population explosion," the solutions which we suggest are to a problem viewed in terms of Western culture and will be developed by the techniques, social and political as well as economic and technological, evolved out of Western culture. The growth and spread of population offer a sense of problem to the Western world not only because of a culturally defined concern with humanity at large but also because of the factors resident in Western culture which center around the idea of progress. We participants in Western society and institutions are concerned, not so much because of the kind of world which we have fashioned for our own generation, but rather because of the better world which we hope to create for those to come. And it will be agreed that population increase is only one of a host of problems with which we must deal effectively in order to achieve the kind of progress toward the "one world" of peace and prosperity we seek.

But because ours is not the only cultural system, because it is possible for human beings to have developed other interpretations and to establish premises different from ours, a potential conflict exists. What, for example, of the culture which seeks a status quo, which welcomes the untrammeled continuation of the present, and repudiates the Western notion of progress? There must then be an infinite variety of different views about something which seems as fundamental as the problem of expanding population.

The point was made long ago that man is a self-domesticated animal. This means that not only have human beings undergone certain physiological changes as a result of living together in society, but also that human cultures have created the conditions under which population optima might flourish. In other words, the human has been able to create conditions suitable to his own increase just as he is able to do so for the animals he has domesticated. But this is only true to a degree; few cultures think in terms of either the advantages or drawbacks to population increase. By domesticating himself, man merely creates the conditions whereby population stability and growth are made possible. In self-domestication, man removes the checks which a balance of nature might otherwise provide. Culture, as the distinguishing human characteristic, is the triumph of man over nature; the various human cultures provide ways in which this conquest may be realized. It follows that as the problem of population emerges, the different cultures will have hit on different solutions. When the ultimate factor in human population growth — that of biological increase and fertility — is considered,

99

it is clear that cultural institutions themselves shape or direct the biological.

It is this point which calls forth the concern of the cultural anthropologist, a concern which is essentially one of comparison, reflecting an interest in the many ways in which various socio-cultural groups of men have solved their problems. The biological fact of reproduction is a denominator common to all mankind but worked upon very differently by different cultural settings. It is curious perhaps that cultural anthropology has had little interest in numbers, in the size of human aggregates. This is less surprising when it is considered that anthropologists' concern is always with the potential variability of human behavior rather than with the relative weighting of one group against another on the basis of the relative sizes of the populations in question. Thus it is perhaps sufficient to compare, from the point of view of kinds of behavior represented, the socio-cultural institutions of such diverse peoples as the Klamath Indians of Oregon, the Maya of Mexico, and, let us say, the Hindus. The Klamath, at the time of contact by Europeans, had a population of perhaps 800; the Maya, in 1520, had well over a million; and the Hindus, today, reach an astronomical population figure. Each people has markedly different social institutions, each is culturally distinct and unique.

In such comparisons, the anthropologist has at hand a virtual "living laboratory," one which justly can be used to evaluate the social and cultural relations to population growth and to fertility in the human being. And it may legitimately be asked, what kinds of cultural forms are productive of population increase? What pre-conditions are necessary to it? A partial answer may be found on each of three different levels: the ecological; the social, referring here to the kinds of organizations which men have fashioned; and the cultural, as we find it resident covertly in value, definition of life, the universe, and so on.

Socio-cultural factors do not of course exist in a vacuum. They relate to numerous features which are in turn derived from nature. The problem of fertility and of size of population is in some measure indistinct from the kinds of ecological adjustment that a human group makes. Environment in the geographical sense is thus part of the picture but not all of it. It is no tautology to say that out of culture culture is bred. The history and development of the many cultural modes of man indicate clearly that it is out of the horizon of culture itself that the forms of culture have their being and origins. There are human adaptations to ecological situations but there are also realms of choice afforded by the background of history. Given an environment in which it might be possible to effect full exploration of one or another resource, why is it that a human group resident there makes one selection but ignores others? Ecology and environment relate to social systems, it is true, and underlie them, but history is also a prime mover. Man indeed is the product of his history and is subject to the determined course in which his history sets him.

In this light, one may justly ask why it is that human populations appear to cluster at the centers of civilization, that marginal cultures, those on the peripheries of such centers, are smaller. Can it be that an upsurge of culture – that which might be called the basis of civilization – has as a necessary prerequisite a large population aggregate? The ancient Near East, China, India appear to have been crossroads, points at which settled riverine populations were subjected to a vigorous influx of new ideas. A discussion of whether the "crossroads" location and the impetus brought about by the acceleration of invention and the diffusion of ideas are in themselves factors in population growth leads again to the consideration of ecological patterns in human society and further to an evaluation of the nature of society itself in its bearing on population.

So-called primitive or, better, non-literate societies may in some measure be considered as marginal developments. Certainly, the history of the primitive world is fully as long as that of civilization, if the latter is defined by its hallmark of writing. Among the non-literate peoples, however, a slower rate of culture change and a closer relation to nature are perceptible. This means that ecological systems may, in their reflection of the more intimate relation of man to nature, contribute to the growth and thereafter the maintenance of optimum populations in defined areas. An example is to be seen among the so-called hunting and gathering peoples, where the human balance and the food supply, as well as the culturally determined ways of exploiting sources of food, clearly place limitations on population growth and where, in fact, a kind of natural selection may be said still to take place. The hunting-gathering society, further, is subject to the limitation that every member of the social unit must become preoccupied with the realization of the society's economic goal, a factor promoting a degree of cultural stagnation since it operates to preclude intensive effort in other directions.

It is only with agriculture that another potential is introduced, a fact which leads V. Gordon Childe to speak of the invention of agriculture in the Neolithic age as the great human revolution. In ecological terms, an agricultural society is the only one which can permit a population increase. It is axiomatic not only that agriculture permits the development of a food surplus, thus allowing a greater population potential, but also that it frees individuals from the economic round, to give vent to aspects of the human inventive genius, thereby creating the basis for increased production and the ultimate conquest of environment which characterizes industrialized societies.

The ecological problem and its relation to population growth can indeed be vastly oversimplified. There are many kinds of human ecological systems which in turn have an intimate relationship to the kinds of social units which men may fashion. There are different kinds of hunting-gathering situations and the hoe cultivator must be set off from the intensive agriculturalist, the settled pastoralist from the pastoral nomad. As one considers the wide belt of pastoralism that extends across Africa and through Asia to the Pacific one becomes aware of a parasitic ecology, one in which animal breeding becomes ancillary to settled intensive agriculture. In such groups, one is struck by the virtual cyclical nature of increase and decline of populations, not so much through natural checks and growths as through the variations of ecological systems brought about, on the margins of China, Anatolia, or Arabia, by shifts of groups to a settled agricultural economy and back again to pastoralism. The results of such ecological shifts, so important in history, are seen in such peoples as the Mongols and the Arabs, or indeed in the migrations of peoples, the so-called Völkerwanderungen, which marked the end of the Roman empire.

One cannot deny the import of ecology to population but at the same time it would be both misleading and erroneous to attribute cultural types to economic, ecological, or environmental circumstances. The historical factors which shape cultures imply the setting of a course in a particular direction and the element of culture becomes significant precisely because it reflects the kinds of choices that humans make. If we apply this to the population problem, it is hardly sufficient to note that the ways of making a living relate to the size of the human aggregate. There are in addition those forms of organization, the social structures, those conventional definitions and common understandings that every people has — their respective cultural systems themselves, in short — which have a precise bearing on the ultimate or optimum group size.

It must be said that there are few cultures which have concerned themselves with a population problem. Rome, of course, counted its citizens and subjects for purposes of taxation, while China, beginning in the latter Han dynasty, counted its people for a labor potential. Somewhat the same thing appears to have happened in Peru of the Incas, where the device of the quipu, knotted cords designed for counting, seems to have sparked the idea. But as one reviews the other historic and non-literate peoples of the world, omitting the concerns about population growth among modern industrialized peoples, it is clear that the population issue as such has no following.

To be sure, a population excess leading to deprivation, famine, or other misfortune offers a problem to any people. Most, however, have resorted to rule of thumb solutions. War seems a universal solution to the problem of population pressures, although the symbols associated with a war effort must inevitably be couched in more concrete terms. To a great extent, the various socio-cultural units of mankind leave the problem to the individual and provide a defined yardstick by which he may measure his actions. Contraception, abortion, infanticide, are treated in a highly variable manner by different cultures. More than this, however, a culture may, through its social institutions and structure, pattern the ways by which increase or decline in population may be effected. And here is to be seen the possible intimacy of relationship between cultural system and size of aggregate.

It is one thing to speak of an ecological system as imposing general limitations on the size of an aggregate. It is quite another to note the ways in which an aggregate may conceive of itself. For, in fact, what is a population? This is no easy question to answer. Language, nation, ethnic group, and a host of other factors, not the least of which is community of territory, must be considered. The present writer, for example, who has done ethnological field work among Eskimo, can point to the fact that there are an estimated 25,000 people speaking an Eskimo language and spread above the 60th parallel from Alaska to eastern Greenland. This figure, useful though it may be to a demographer, has no cultural reality. The writer must say that he has carried on his investigations among a specific group with a defined set of cultural norms and a specific in-group consciousness. Only then is a meaningful statement about the population made. If the Eskimo group in question is defined as that of northern Alaska it is possible to offer a statement not only as to the peculiar ecological situation developed here but also as to why there is justification for considering this segment of the people known as the Eskimo as a culture and as a population.

For purposes of the analysis of the cultural relations to population, then, it is necessary to define the population which so sees itself. Without adopting a wholly mechanistic view of culture, it seems safe to say that a socio-cultural organization virtually has a life of its own. No individual can fully share in the totality of skills, specialties, or experiences which his culture offers. But a culture does offer the set of boundaries of the familiar and becomes meaningful because it does offer a basis for predictability. In setting limits to human behavior, a cultural system works to provide stability and ease from tension for its participating members.

Among the North Alaskan Eskimo, for example, before the cultural disruption caused by the advent of Europeans, there were two ecological systems, one based on sea mammal hunting, the other on inland caribou hunting in nomadic bands. Between the two systems a delicate balance existed, an interdependence fostered by trade of goods which each needed to survive. Hence, although much of the way of life was dictated by economic specialization, the choice was made to create a set of common understandings through kinship on the one hand and trading partnerships on the other. In this way, 3,000 nomadic Eskimo were solidified by the bands of kinship which pervaded their area and they in turn set themselves off from the 1,000 maritime Eskimo who were likewise distinguished by their web of social relations. In each group there ran established kinship usages and the economic balance between them was maintained by trading partnerships in which the social ties were constantly being reaffirmed. One of the ways in which this was done was by temporary wife exchange between partners of different ecological settings. This situation of balanced economy served to define the cultural unit.

Archaeological evidence seems to substantiate that the populations in question remained stable over a long period of time. The socioeconomic balance precluded migration on any scale and if the fertility rate was high, there was a high accident rate in the arduous Arctic environment and infanticide in times of stress. In regard to this culture, it is possible to define a population and to see the cultural factors which maintained it.

As one therefore reviews the remarkable diversity of human behavior, considering the world before the greater population following industrialization, can the "living laboratory" provide additional insight into the relations between culture and population? It has been shown that very few societies are concerned with increase or, in fact, with decrease in population. For a worldwide comparison, one must look to the culturally sanctioned practices arising out of the phenomenon of reproduction, since obviously it is at this level that population problems begin. It must be regarded as axiomatic that reproductive practices are parts of any total social structure. They do not exist as vacuums nor are there universal attitudes. It is nonsense, for example, to speak of a desire for offspring as common to all societies or of a quasi-instinctive "mother-love" in the human being. One must recognize that there are highly variable definitions of offspring, different motives in different groups for paternity, and remarkably different statuses and roles accorded to both parent and child in various cultures. It is possible only to conclude that the desire for offspring is learned and that the phenomenon of parenthood is subject to vastly differing kinds of interpretation.

One runs a gamut from the overt denial of physiological paternity, on the basis of cultural definition, which is reported for the many tribes of native Australians and the Trobriand Islanders, to the paternalism of the Chinese family, where the ancestral cult and Confucian reasoning make failure to produce offspring a cardinal sin. Or one may go to the Marquesas Islanders where the child is viewed as an unfortunate accident who interferes with his mother's social affairs and is shoved off to the care of an older person. And even among ourselves, there is clearly a cultural question involved in reproduction, although we have lost the emphasis on family line, on inheritance of property, and on the notion that the child provides aid to his aged parents. The American family, atomistic though it has become, finds a basis for its existence in offspring, in the mere having of them, and in the kinds of social-prestige relations which our society permits the family with children to develop. Not the least of this is the opportunity for display which the child affords. Unlike many other cultures, twentieth-century America has chosen to idealize the child's world and to make childhood almost an end in itself.

All this being so, it remains to ask if there are certain kinds of social institutions which promote greater fertility and larger populations. Obviously, industrialized society such as has developed in the West does encourage population growth, not only by providing the conditions which disrupt a natural balance, but also because of the cult of the individual which ascribes worth to individual human life. And it cannot be denied that the phenomenal population expansions of both China and India since 1800 are directly attributable to Western influences in these areas.

It has been contended that certain types of social organization are more conducive to fertility increase. A recent UNESCO survey of this subject made some pertinent if rather inconclusive suggestions. One might suppose, for example, that polygynous unions would increase the population in the socio-cultural system that sanctions them. But it seems doubtful that this is the case. Given a roughly equal balance between the sexes in any society, uncontrolled polygyny is no practical solution in the problem of societal perpetuation. True, it has taken place in conquest situations and it is wholly possible where certain sanctions exist, such as in a levirate organization where the men have a responsibility for the females in the family of a deceased relative. But while it is possible to put forth hypotheses to the effect that paternal, polygynous institutions are conducive to a higher birth rate, it seems that this is an argument after the fact. One thinks at once of China, of course, but conversely India, while it possesses its share of groups organized as paternal lineages, nevertheless has an infinite number of subgroupings with matrilineal institutions. The phenomenal growth of the West in the last century is also linked with another social type, that of individualism and monogamy. Other examples might be given, but it may be questioned that there is any direct or necessary correlation between type of social structure and population.

A correlation between culture and population seems to be far more subtle and to lie not so much in the kind of structure which a society creates as in the somewhat more elusive factors of cultural norms, in short, in the kinds of premises or postulates which are inherent in any cultural system. Thus while growth and expansion of population are concomitants of the biological phenomenon of fertility, man, far removed as a result of his self-domestication from mere biological cause and effect, creates patterns of thought and behavior which have the end result of controlling his own biology. It is recognized that various pathological conditions — hypertension, psychosomatic illness, incidence of virtually any pathological state — have a direct relation to the force of culture. So also is it apparent that the man-made conditioning of culture has a direct bearing on human fertility. The UNESCO study mentioned earlier points to the fact that a stable culture has a higher rate of fertility, regardless of the kind of kinship, societal, or formal structure which has been created. It appears axiomatic that if a culture satisfies the needs of its members, providing them with a comprehensible basis for living, meeting the human component of need in satisfactory and predictable ways, such a culture will thrive and flourish, holding its own at least in terms of gross natality. As our Western cultures have made inroads on those of other peoples, we have seen not infrequently decline and decay, the loss of what has been called the "will to live" and the consequent decimation of populations. Cultural vigor, coupled with stability of the natural environment and human control of it, appears to be able to effect man's rise both in stability and in numbers.

No corollary of this point is suggested and no application sought. In culture man finds the why and wherefore of his own desire for life and the increase of his kind. The point suggests merely that there are many ways of reaching the same goal and that awareness of them provides some further basis for man's perspective on himself.

Variations on a Theme by Malthus

THEORIES OF POPULATION PRESSURE ON FOOD SUPPLIES

THE Malthusian theory of population envisaged man as being driven to the subsistence level by the constant pressure of population on the earth's limited food supply. Man's propensity to procreate would lead to a recurring situation in which there were more mouths to feed than could be fed, and famine and pestilence would be the means by which the population would be held within the limits of the available food supply. Mortality and food prices would both be high.

The history of the world economy since Malthus' day has belied his vision in each respect. The number of people in the world has increased dramatically, while mortality has fallen the world over, and practically everywhere levels of living have risen. Food prices, in terms of human effort, have dropped drastically, and they have probably also fallen relative to the prices of other goods and services.

The reasons for the failure of the Malthusian hypothesis are well known. New lands were opened up in America and Australia, and, even more important, techniques of cultivation were improved. Improvements in technique made it possible to obtain more food from a given amount of land with a given amount of other resources. As an example of the dramatic nature of the advance in agricultural technology, one can cite the history of United States agriculture from 1910 to the present. During this period the agricultural output has about doubled while the number of farmers has grown by about 25 per cent and the land area under cultivation has remained substantially constant. Capital equipment, to be sure, has been added, but even when this element has been taken into account more than half of the observed increase in output remains unexplained, and this must be attributed to improved techniques.[1]

Prospects for the future are also good. Agricultural experts are confident that world food production can be increased by 50 per cent in the next twenty-five years and by 100 per cent in the next fifty years. Indeed, a doubling of the world's food output is possible even with presently known techniques, though it could not be achieved within a decade or two without a substantial rise in the relative price of food. Over the longer run agricultural prices will probably not rise substantially. If agriculture shares equally with industry in the fruits of technical advance, levels of per capita productivity in both sectors will tend to rise in the same proportion, and with them per capita incomes. It is a well-established fact, however, that as per capita incomes rise the proportion spent on purchases from farmers falls. Thus, with equal increases in per capita productivity in both sectors, there would be set in motion a tendency to attract resources out of agriculture and into industry. This tendency is reflected in the market by a differential between the incomes that can be earned in the two sectors — a differential favorable to the industrial sector. Such a differential has been characteristic of most countries in the process of economic development, and today characterizes practically every country in the world.

The differential between agricultural and nonagricultural incomes is relevant in assessing a second, and more optimistic, version of the Malthusian theory. In this version, the possibility that standards of living might stabilize considerably above the crude "subsistence" level was analyzed. People were viewed as voluntarily limiting their families, by "moral restraint," so as to maintain a customary standard of life. Population growth would stop before pressing fully against the food-producing capacity of the world.

The mechanics of this theory were not fully worked out by its proponents. Needless to say, they cannot be the same as those of Malthus' original version, since famine and pestilence are here ruled out. It is not difficult, however, for a modern economist to fill in the gaps. The complete theory would then run something like this: The number of children desired by the typical family will vary with its level of income, being greater for high levels of income than for low levels. At some

[1] T. W. Schultz, *The Economic Organization of Agriculture* (New York: McGraw-Hill, 1953), pp. 108ff.

level of income, known as the "customary" level, the typical family will produce just enough children to keep the total population constant. If average family income falls below this level, population will decline, tending to raise average income back up to the "customary" level; if average income rises above the customary level, population will rise, exerting pressure on the limited food-producing capacity and tending to lower incomes back down to the customary level. Over time, people's tastes could change, and the customary level of living could rise. Progress of this kind would, of course, be possible only with a declining population in the absence of improvements in technique.

Let us now examine the role of the differential between agricultural and nonagricultural incomes in the context of this "Malthusian" theory. Assume that by some "act of God" population is reduced below its equilibrium level. Average family incomes rise while the demand for food falls below its previous level. Expenditures are diverted from farm products to other things, setting off a movement of resources from the land to the factory and creating an income differential in favor of industrial workers. However, the higher family income levels lead in the course of time to more children per family. At this point the demand for food increases relative to other things, and a movement of resources back to the farm is called for. The income differential now turns in favor of agricultural workers. In short, Malthusian pressure — the pressure of population on the food supply — is, even in the optimistic version of Malthus' theory, associated with resource movements out of industry and toward agriculture and with an income differential which favors agricultural activity.

We do not now observe such movements, and even for the long-term future, movements of resources in the reverse direction appear to be in prospect. Furthermore, if technical advance is present, movements of resources out of industry and into agriculture can exist without Malthusian pressure being present since technical advance makes possible the production of the same quantity of goods with fewer resources. One can say, in a sense, that resources are "freed" by technical advance. If the advance takes place wholly in the industrial sector, and population is constant, the freed resources will represent an increase in per capita real income. This increase will in part be spent on agricultural products, and some of the freed resources will be drawn into agriculture to add to production. But under these circumstances there would be no decline in per capita real income and no "Malthusian pressure." So long as it does not take all the resources freed by technical advance in the industrial sector in order to produce the extra farm products needed to maintain per capita food consumption, levels of living will rise in spite of rising food prices and movements of resources from the city to the farm. The more rapid the rate of progress in per capita productivity in nonfarming activities, the higher is the rate at which farm prices can rise without jeopardizing standards of living. And, as will be pointed out in some detail in subsequent sections of this paper, the prospects for continued advances in productivity are very good indeed.

It may be instructive to examine the implications of the preceding analysis for different parts of the world. One often finds a distinction drawn between the so-called underdeveloped countries, where Malthusian pressure is alleged to exist, and the more advanced economies of the Western world, where such pressure is asserted to be absent. It is my contention that the lack of more rapid economic progress in the underdeveloped countries is not due principally to the pressure of population on land resources, but rather stems from the general poverty of these areas and the lack of facility among their people for adopting new methods of production.

Much of the discussion on this subject has been clouded by the misconception that a country's food supply somehow "ought" to be found within its own borders. In point of fact, some of the most advanced economies of the world are among the least self-sufficient in terms of food. Sweden, Belgium, and Switzerland maintain high and rising standards of living in spite of substantial dependence on foreign sources of food. Their progress has been achieved through improvement in the quantity and quality of their capital equipment and through the rising productive capacities of their labor. Similar avenues to progress are open to the presently underdeveloped countries, and indeed are being currently explored in many of them. The advance of these economies is hindered by their very poverty, which makes it difficult for them to accumulate rapidly the capital equipment or to acquire rapidly the skilled labor force that will make them more productive. This barrier to development has been present regardless of whether land resources were relatively abundant, as in the case of Brazil, or relatively scarce, as in India. It is, I believe, together with rigidities of habit and social organization which inhibit the adoption of new techniques, the fundamental deterrent to economic development.

Since there is a world market for most products, agricultural or industrial, the pressure of population on food supplies, if it is to exist at all, will be a world phenomenon, not one associated with a particular country. Should such pressure emerge, it will have the consequence of bidding up the prices of primary products and the incomes of primary-producing countries, and may accordingly be welcomed rather than dreaded by the underdeveloped parts of the world.

PRESSURES ON RAW MATERIALS

In recent years the fear arose in some quarters that continued world economic progress was threatened by the pressure of increasing demands on limited supplies of raw materials, here taking the role that for Malthus was played by limited food supplies. The prospects that the world's material-producing potential would not be sufficient to permit economic growth and new rises in living standards were exhaustively analyzed in *Resources for Freedom*, the five-volume report of the President's Materials Policy Commission.

The initial stimulus which gave rise to the commission's appointment was, as might be expected, the great boom in materials prices that followed the outbreak of war in Korea. Many responsible citizens, in and out of government, were frankly frightened. If what was clearly a minor war could double or more than double the prices of critical materials, what would happen to these prices over time as the steady pressures of economic growth led to constantly increasing demands for materials? Indeed, it was conceivable that shortages of crucial materials might even prevent the continued material progress of our economy and greatly inhibit its military power.

The commission's report had the effect of dispelling any fears of really serious and prolonged materials shortages over the next two or three decades. The sharp price rises of the Korean War period were, in the commission's opinion, the reflection of a rapid short-run increase in demand for all classes of materials; in the longer run supplies could and would be expanded, greatly limiting the extent of price increases. After estimating that the materials consumption of the United States would rise by some 65 per cent between 1950 and 1975, the commission judged that for only a few materials was there any strong basis for anticipating a substantial rise in relative price. Even in these cases, of which copper and lead are examples, the availability of abundant substitutes (such as aluminum and plastics) would limit both the extent of price rise and the costliness to society of the underlying "shortages."

In the past the United States economy had grown greatly; its materials consumption had increased 150 per cent since the turn of the century; and yet by 1950 the relative price of raw materials had not risen appreciably. The factors of technology, discovery, and substitution had combined to bring about this result. In the case of copper, United States output had tripled since 1900; but in spite of the fact that the copper content of the ores being mined had been cut to a third of their earlier level, technological advances had enabled output per man hour to multiply by four, and the price of copper relative to other things to be cut in half. In petroleum, in spite of perennial scares to the effect that our reserves would last only twelve or thirteen more years, output increased to more than fifty times the 1900 figure and to more than five times the 1920 figure, while new reserves were discovered more rapidly than the old ones were used up. Technology made possible the substitution of other materials for tin in the making of collapsible tubes and foil, in great economies in tinplating, in the substitution of aluminum for copper in long-distance electrical transmission lines, and in increases in the efficiency with which power was obtained from coal.

Substitutions similar to those observed in the past are always available, once prices change sufficiently to make them economic. It would not take a great rise in the price of petroleum to make worth while the production of petroleum from oil shale, of which our economy possesses vast reserves. And even if these reserves should one day be depleted a modest further rise in price would encourage the production of oil from coal, of which our economy possesses something like a thousand years' supply. Although our deposits of high-grade iron ore are running out, the production of steel from our vast supplies of lower grade taconite ore has already proved possible.

It is indeed astounding how the existence of a few materials in real abundance can ease pressures throughout our materials economy. Our riches of coal and shale mean that lack of oil will not be a bottleneck to economic progress. Oil, in turn, is used to make synthetic rubber, which frees us from dependence on supplies of natural rubber, and plastics which can substitute for tin in containers, for copper and lead in pipes, and for a great many other metal products. Aluminum, one of the most abundant of minerals, stands ready to take over nearly all the electrical uses of copper should supplies of the latter begin to fail.

The conclusion of the commission's analysis was that there would be no major upward pressure on materials prices in the United States and the free world within the time horizon studied. Surely the forces envisaged as working to limit materials shortages in the period until 1975 will still be operative thereafter, but it is nevertheless instructive to inquire at what rate materials prices would have to rise, at some hypothetical future time, in order for the advance of living standards to be halted. Assume an economy in which per capita productivity in nonmineral industries is increasing at 1½ per cent per year, and in which, as in the United States in the recent past, expenditures on mineral products amount to about 3 per cent of the national income. It would take fantastic increases in mineral prices, amounting in the first instance to almost 50 per cent per year, in order to wipe out the positive effect on levels of living caused by the improvement in productivity in the nonmineral sectors of the economy. The effect of a trebling of minerals prices on living standards would be wiped out by merely four years of normal productivity growth. It is difficult indeed to imagine, in these circumstances, that minerals shortages are likely to be a seriously limiting factor to population growth or improvement in levels of living in the foreseeable future.

POPULATION PRESSURE ON PER CAPITA INCOME GROWTH

We have seen that neither limitations of food-producing capacity nor minerals shortages are likely to limit world population growth in the half-century or so ahead. We have also seen that individual countries need not produce their own food or materials supplies; hence there is no reason to look especially to these factors in the search for what may limit a given country's population growth. The rate at which a country with a given level of population may advance in standards of living, and the rate at which a country may increase in population without lowering its standard of living, are determined by the factors which influence the country's total economic productivity. Part of a country's increase in output stems from population increase, or more precisely increase in the amount of labor used in production, but another part, crucial to the present analysis, stems from other sources.

For the moment I shall merely list the other sources; they will be discussed in greater detail in the next section. First, there is the increase in the country's stock of useful capital equipment; the more rapid this increase, the more rapid, other things being equal, will be the growth in output per head or the rate at which population can grow without a fall in income per head. Second, there is the productivity of capital equipment. In countries where capital is scarce, it is normally highly productive; such countries can get as much extra output from a small increment to their capital stock as other, more capital-abundant countries get from a large increment to capital stock. Third, there is the rate of technological advance. The adoption of more efficient methods of production makes it possible for a country to get more output from the same amounts of labor and capital equipment. Countries which succeed in achieving high rates of technological advance accordingly can grow more rapidly in either population or living standard or both than countries in otherwise similar circumstances which do not have rapid technical progress.

In this section I shall assume that these three factors can be lumped together, yielding for any country the rate at which income per head would grow if there were no increase in the active labor force. Let us say this rate is R per cent per year. Total output of the country will, of course, grow at a faster rate than R per cent per year if there are increments to the labor force. But in general, the greater the increase in the labor force, the lower will be per capita income. Suppose that a country produced last year a total output of 100, and that R is 2 per cent, so that in the absence of any increase in the labor force output this year would be 102. If now there is an increase of 1 per cent in the labor force, output will be higher than 102. But we can be quite certain that output will not be as high as 103, for a 1 per cent increase in the labor force would bring about a 1 per cent increase in output only if labor were the only important agent of production. In point of fact, the share of labor in the national incomes of countries varies roughly between one half and three quarters. This suggests that a 1 per cent increase in the labor force in our example would raise output this year from 102 to somewhere between 102½ and 102¾. New members of the labor force will presumably receive in wages an amount closely approximating their addition to the value of national output, and there is every reason to expect that their wages will not differ appreciably from those earned by workers already in the labor force.

The percentage increase in output — hence the degree to which a population may increase or to which a standard of living may rise — depends on "Labor" and "Capital," to use good terms roughly. Actually, this increase in output depends on the increase in income going to labor and on the increase in technology. The increase in income going to labor depends on two things: the percentage increase in the labor force — we denote this by "L"; and the fraction of the national income going to labor — this is denoted by "F." The increase in output attributable to "Labor" is found by multiplying F and L. "R" denotes the rate of technological advance. The percentage increase in output is simply a sum of these rates. To use symbols, letting Y stand for the percentage increase in output, $Y = FL + R$. Nothing has been added or taken away. We are just employing the economy of expression found in an equation.

Now we may turn to the question, at how large a rate may a country's population grow without a reduction in the standard of living? This question is most simply answered if we ignore the problems connected with a transition from one birth rate to another, and simply assume that the rates of increase in population and in the labor force are equal. Under this assumption, we know that per capita income will be constant when Y is equal to L, will be rising when Y is greater than L, and falling when Y is less than L. The critical case for answering the question is, of course, that in which Y is equal to L; the maximum rate of growth of population consistent with maintenance of the standard of living turns out to be $R/(1 - F)$, as can be seen by setting Y equal to L in the above equation. Now $1 - F$ ought not shock anyone: this is simply the fraction of national income *not* going to labor.

I should like now to illustrate the above formulation by two examples. The first will be of a "typical" developed and growing economy, modeled broadly after the United States, and the second will be of a more or less stagnant underdeveloped economy, modeled broadly after India in the period between the world wars. In the developed and growing economy the fraction of the national income going to labor is two thirds or greater, so the $(1 - F)$ is one third or less. The observed rate of growth of output is about 3 per cent per year, and the rate of growth of the labor force is between 1 and 1½ per cent per year; these two facts imply that R is in the order of 2 per cent per year. Thus we see that for this developed economy R/(1 − F) will be 6 per cent per year or greater; that is, population could grow at any rate up to 6 per cent per year, and even possibly more, without causing a decline in living standards. Since people in countries like the United States do not in any case choose to multiply at a rate of 6 per cent per year, living standards rise and "Malthusian" problems are absent.

Next let us consider the case of an underdeveloped economy. Often in such economies the fraction of the national income going to labor is around one half, the rate of increase in the labor force is about 1 to 2 per cent per year, and national income is rising by no more than 2½ per cent per year. R is thus about 1½ per cent per year, while 1/(1 − F) is around 2. Here the maximum rate of population increase consistent with stable or rising living standards is but 3 per cent per year. If one can judge from the poor data available on the underdeveloped countries, there have been a number of cases and periods when living standards have remained stable while population increased at 1½ per cent per year or less. In these situations one can infer that R must have been three eighths or less. These are the cases that have been frequently characterized as "Malthusian." It is my contention that the factors which created "Malthusian" situations in these instances were the factors making for a low R, rather than factors directly connected with limitations on food or materials production.

THE ROLE OF TECHNOLOGICAL PROGRESS

It is easy to see how R, the rate at which national output would advance if there were no increase in the labor force, depends upon the rate of additions to capital equipment. If national income were 100 last year, and if net investment were made in the amount of 10, output this year would be 101, with the same labor force, if the investment had a productivity in real terms of 10 per cent, or 102 if the investment had a productivity of 20 per cent. The available evidence suggests that in the United States economy the productivity of capital is in the order of 10 per cent, and over the past the rate of net investment out of national income has also been about 10 per cent on the average. Hence one might anticipate from this source an annual increment of output in the order of 1 per cent.

For other economies the relevant figures have been quite different. Western Germany and Japan, since the war, appear to have been investing close to 15 per cent of their national income in capital assets, and it also seems likely that the productivity of capital in these countries is substantially greater than in the United States. With a productivity of capital of 15 to 20 per cent, the rate of net investment maintained by Germany and Japan in recent years would lead to an increase of output of 2¼ to 3 per cent, even in the absence of increases in the labor force. On the other hand, in the case of Chile, net investment appears to have averaged only 3 or 4 per cent of the national income over the last decade or so; even with a productivity of capital as high as 20 per cent, therefore, investment could bring about a .6 to .8 per cent annual increment in output.

We now turn to a more puzzling component of R — technological advance. Suppose an economy in which output is growing at 3 per cent per year, the labor force at 1 per cent, and in which 10 per cent of the national income is invested with a productivity of 10 per cent. Assume the share of labor in the national income is two thirds. The increase in the labor force will accordingly "explain" a two thirds of 1 per cent annual increment in output, while investment will "explain" a 1 per cent increment. The 1⅓ per cent annual increment in output which is not explained by these two factors we shall label as being due to improved technology.

It should be evident from the above example that "improved technology" is merely a catchall term to cover the influences of a multitude of forces. Improved technology, in our sense, may come from the invention or application of new techniques, to be sure, but it may also result from improvement in the quality of the labor force (through education or on-the-job training), or even from the simple movement of workers from low-wage (i.e. low-productivity) to high-wage areas or industries. Furthermore, it is difficult to draw the line between what is here called the productivity of capital and what is called technological improvement. When a new method is discovered and developed, its initial applications are often highly profitable. Fortunes have been made within a few years, starting almost from scratch, through the exploitation of a single good idea. These cases might be viewed as instances in which capital investments were paying off at, say, 100 per cent per year for a time, and one might be tempted to say that the economic growth arising from these investments was not due to technological advance but simply to the payoff on capital investment. I believe that this interpretation obscures the issue at hand. If the normal rate of return to capital is 10 per cent, and a new technique makes it possible to earn 100 per cent in a certain line, it is the new technique which is responsible for 90 per cent of the earnings of capital in the new field, and this amount should be rightly attributed to technological advance.

One should not conclude, however, that technological advance is always reflected in high earnings on the particular sums which are invested in new lines. Sometimes competition enters rapidly, sometimes slowly, but the normal end result of technological advance is not an increased rate of return on capital but rather a reduction in the real price which consumers have to pay for the product in which the improvement occurred. Hence it would not be appropriate to measure the contribution of new techniques only by the excess over the normal rate of return on capital which is earned in the fields of their application.

In spite of the several ways in which what we have called technological advance may come about, there appear to be severe limits on the rate of advance that any economy can achieve. The main reason for this is that technological advance is rarely without its price. It is costly to improve the skill of the labor force, and costly to develop new methods. Sometimes one observes inventions which greatly add to productivity and which appear to have been the result of a "brainstorm" rather than of conscious and expensive research. But before drawing the conclusion that these improvements are in some sense "free," one should realize that much of the daily work of production managers and business executives in general is precisely to try to think up ways in which pennies and dollars can be saved by making production more efficient. These efforts tend to pay off in part in a steady stream of minor improvements, and in part in intermittent and more dramatic major improvements. The mere fact that dramatic improvements are relatively rare suggests that finding them is not an easy job.

Even improvements which result from the movement of workers to more productive employments may be quite costly to achieve. Particularly in underdeveloped economies the ties that bind workers to their traditional homes and ways of life have proved difficult to break, as have the habits of production ingrained sometimes by centuries of traditional practice. Perhaps the only really cheap avenue to more efficient production is the elimination of legal impediments. All countries, in varying degrees, have legislation that operates to shelter and foster lines of production which by normal economic standards would be inefficient — tariffs, subsidies, import quotas, multiple exchange rate systems, are examples of such schemes of economic policy. Since the repeal or alteration of legislation has very little economic cost, advances in productivity stemming from such changes may indeed be regarded as cheaply bought. Still, such advances may not take place very rapidly in time, for the improvement coming from the elimination of protection for an inefficient industry is contingent on the movement of resources from it to more efficient industries, and this movement may itself be sluggish.

The fact that major new discoveries are comparatively infrequent means that in any given period of time some industries will show very large rates of technological advance as compared with the average of all industries. Thus, for example, in the decade 1919–29, technological advance took place in the rubber products industry of the United States at a rate of close to 9 per cent per year. By the end of this period it was possible to obtain more than twice as much output from a given amount of capital and labor as it was at the beginning. During the same period the rate of technological advance was about 5 per cent per year in motor vehicles and tobacco products, and only about 2½ per cent per year for United States manufacturing as a whole. These estimates are based on data presented by Daniel Creamer.[2] For the United States economy as a whole, the rate of technological advance was even lower. Abramovitz, working from Kuznets' and Kendrick's data, estimated that the improvement in national output due to technological advance was less than 2 per cent per year during this same period; indeed, according to Abramovitz' figures, the rate of 2 per cent per annum was only exceeded in this century during the period immediately surrounding World War I.[3]

[2] Daniel Creamer, *Capital and Output Trends in Manufacturing Industries, 1880–1948* (New York: National Bureau of Economic Research, Occasional Paper No. 41, 1954).

[3] Moses Abramovitz, "Resource and Output Trends in the United States since 1870," *American Economic Review*, May 1956, p. 18.

ARNOLD C. HARBERGER

A recent study by Kendrick confirms the impression that outstanding improvements in technology are rare events, and that for the economy as a whole the pace of technological advance is normally rather modest. Kendrick studied 33 industry groups from 1899 to 1953. He divided the period into six subperiods, each roughly a decade in length, and for each group he calculated the rate of technological advance in each of the subperiods. He thus ended with 198 estimates of rates of technological advance of particular industries during roughly decade-long periods. Only 22 of these rates were greater than 5 per cent per annum. When the period from 1899 to 1953 is taken as a whole, only one industry out of the 33 showed technological advance at a rate greater than 5 per cent per annum. The average rate of advance for all 33 industries over the whole period was 2.3 per cent per year, while Kendrick's estimate of the average rate of advance for the entire United States economy over the same period was 1.7 per cent per year.[4]

I have attempted, from the available data, to estimate the rates of technological advance that have characterized the economies of certain important countries in the years following World War II. The data, in general, do not warrant that great precision be attributed to the estimates; but as orders-of-magnitude the estimates appear to be reasonably reliable. Roughly speaking, the rate of technological advance has been in the order of 4 per cent in Western Germany and Japan in the postwar period, about 1½ per cent in Canada, and about 1 per cent in the United States, the United Kingdom, and Chile. To the best of my knowledge, the 4 per cent rates estimated for Western Germany and Japan are without precedent for major countries, but one should recall that these economies ended the war with considerable internal disruptions and dislocations. In each case, small adjustments in critical places permitted great advances in total production. The experiences of these two economies must accordingly, I feel, be regarded as unlikely of duplication in more normal circumstances. I believe that a sustained rate of technological improvement in the order of 2 per cent per annum must be regarded as an excellent performance for any country.

[4] John W. Kendrick, *Productivity Trends: Capital and Labor* (New York: National Bureau of Economic Research, Occasional Paper No. 53, 1956).

The Population Ahead

THE FUTURE FOR ADVANCED AND UNDERDEVELOPED
ECONOMIES

Let us now try to pull together the strands of this analysis. We found that the maximum rate of population growth achievable by an economy without reduction in living standards was $R/(1-F)$. Then we lumped the components of R together. We saw that R was composed of three factors: (1) The rate of net investment out of national income in a given economy, which we call "I." (2) The productivity of the new investment; call this "P." (3) Finally, the rate of technological advance — designated by "T." R includes all three — but in what combination? Clearly, the rate of investment and of productivity belong together: the product of I and P measures the rate of productive investment. Then R is simply a sum of two rates — the investment rate found by multiplying I and P, and the rate called "T." To use symbols, $R = (IP + T)$. Earlier, we saw the maximum rate of population growth — the rate at which Malthusian pressure becomes severe — was $Y = R/1 - F$. It takes no mathematical genius to substitute for R so that $Y = (IP + T)/(1 - F)$.

Developed countries are shown by this relation to be in a peculiarly favorable position. In these countries labor is typically a relatively scarce resource, getting something like two thirds or three fourths of the national income; hence the factor $1/(1 - F)$ amounts for these countries to 3 or 4. Furthermore, the developed countries, being wealthy, are in a position to invest in productive capital a rather large fraction of their national incomes; I may be 10 or even 15. Finally their economies have become, in the process of development, adapted to change, and they are able to devote proportionally more of their resources than underdeveloped countries to education and training and research. For them, T will normally be 1 per cent or greater. The one fly in the ointment for the developed economies is that new investment is for them not so productive as for the less developed countries. P will ordinarily not be greater than 15 per cent, and perhaps more normally will be around 10 per cent. The net result of these rough figures is that Malthusian pressure will not set in for a "typical" developed economy until population is growing by at least 6 per cent per year, and may not set in until population grows at 10 per cent a year or more.

The underdeveloped countries, on the other hand, are handicapped

122

by the low productivity of labor. For them, F is typically between .5 and .6, so that $1/(1-F)$ is between 2 and 2½. Furthermore, since they are poor, it is difficult for them to invest as much as 10 per cent of their national incomes in new capital equipment, and also difficult for them to devote as large a fraction of their resources to education, training, and research as the developed countries. Finally, many of them are burdened by institutional and traditional rigidities; they have not become, like the developed countries, adapted to economic change and progress. There are, however, two rays of hope for these countries. The first is the fact that in their economies, capital investment is highly productive; P may well be around 20 per cent in a typical underdeveloped country. The second stems from the fact that these economies are not in the vanguard of technical progress; they have the opportunity to borrow technologies already developed in other parts of the world. In this, however, they are often handicapped by the fact that the technologies developed for advanced economies are suited to situations where capital is cheap and labor is dear, the precise opposite of the case for underdeveloped areas.

An underdeveloped country without technological advance, investing 5 per cent of its national income in capital equipment with a productivity of 20 per cent, can grow in population at no more than 2 or 2½ per cent per year without reducing living standards. A rate of technical advance of 1 per cent will raise these limits to 4–5 per cent, and a rate of technical advance of 2 per cent will raise them to 6–7½ per cent.

The moral of the story is simple. Advanced economies are for many decades to come insulated from Malthusian pressures; the "natural" advance of their productive capacity will provide, at rising living standards, for any population increase they might conceivably choose to produce. Underdeveloped economies are not so insulated. In the absence of technical progress they are likely to be perilously close to the point at which their natural rate of increase of population will doom them to lower levels of living. "Forced draft" investment can help them, for incremental capital is highly productive, but such investment can be bought only at the price of a reduction in their already low living levels. The remaining hope is technological progress. Such progress is itself expensive. It is in considerable part the result of investment in education, training, and research, which, like investment in physical capital, can be bought only by a reduction in living levels. But in part it is the result of improvement in the methods and organization of production. Such improvement is possible for under-developed areas, but it is limited by the rigidity of institutional, cultural, and traditional modes. The degree to which Malthusian pressures will plague the generations immediately ahead will depend upon the degree to which these modes yield to the now universal desire for economic advancement.

Commentary

RATHER than disturb the progressive development of the major themes in this volume, the several discussions that followed the presentation of the papers at the symposium have been gathered into one section. Not all the discussants prepared their comments in a formal sense. Those who did will find their statements reproduced in full in the context of this chapter. The discussions that were not formally written were preserved on tape. The editor listened to these recordings several times and then attempted to report the gist of each of the sessions with as much of the flavor as possible. Since some of the discussants were interrupted by questions, this kind of presentation will be smoother than a verbatim account. In each instance, the reader will be given a clue to the point at issue.

Professor Warren Thompson, dean of American demographers, had been present at the first Minnesota symposium on population and had participated therein. To bring the current discussions into historical perspective, he compared the knowledge and awareness of population problems in the two periods of time. This is an important and difficult task, for in the hindsight of moving history, we find that some earlier estimates of these problems were in error.

Warren S. Thompson:

There are, of course, some major differences between this symposium and the one held in 1948. The type of sessions planned for the current meetings reflects these differences. In part, there is a changed sense of problem, a concern for different aspects of population policy. In part, the differences result from the added knowledge which is the heritage of the present symposium. It is true that some of the estimates made in 1948 have turned out to be erroneous; the error appears greater in the light of the knowledge we have now but which we earlier lacked.

The war had then been over for some three years. There had been relatively high war losses, with the result that death rates had been high; but a decline in the death rate appeared probable, and it was reasonable to assume, in 1948, that there would be increased rates of growth. For one thing man's control of infectious diseases had developed to a remarkable extent. When that control was applied to the underdeveloped countries there would be a great decline in the death rate. Of course, this requires us to qualify the potential growth in terms of the food supply, a qualification always necessary in any discussion of an increasing "rate of natural increase."

By 1948 it was clear that a new interest in health work existed in many countries where no such interest had existed before the war. Consider Japan: with a high birth rate of around 34 per thousand, she stood on the threshold of an unprecedented population growth. Intestinal diseases were being controlled by a new method. "Mass inoculations" required little coercion. The efficiency of DDT and antibiotics in control of infections was known because of our war experience. And the significance of BCG for tuberculosis was also known. But no one realized their full potentialities in 1948.

It was clear, by 1948, that the death rates in the nonindustrial countries could be made to decline — but no one knew how rapidly. No one knew how well the controls effected by such agents as DDT would be accepted. No one fully realized that mass public health controls would produce such rapid and widespread results. Japan, which is not a "nonindustrial" country, had a crude death rate of 8.9 in 1952 — half of that which existed in 1946. Ceylon, perhaps a better example, had a death rate of only 10.4 in 1954 — half of its 1946 rate. These changes were hardly predictable in 1948.

In 1948 the relatively high birth rates of the years 1946, 1947, and 1948 were of course noted. They seemed insignificant since World War I had shown a similar increase. It appeared likely that a decline would occur. There was no reason in 1948 to predict otherwise. And there was a decline in some countries. Japan cut her birth rate from 34 per thousand in 1946 to less than 20 in 1955 (a remarkable decline).

But because her death rate fell even faster she still has an increase in population of about 1,000,000 a year.

Incidentally, there are no examples of declining birth rate in countries where contraception was not practiced before the war, although there are today some signs that contraceptive control will spread faster now than in 1948. We find that in India, for example, the government has taken official cognizance of the problem and is making attempts to develop birth control clinics, to encourage family planning, and so on. But there is today no observed decline in her population. Communist China, too, has been forced to take steps in controlling birth. It now is officially committed to spreading knowledge about birth control practices.

This official recognition by the world's two most populous countries did not exist in 1948. It may be, however, that improved public health work will lead to greater population increases, despite any attempt in such countries to increase the use of contraceptive devices and thus lower the birth rate.

The program planned for 1948 seemed to reflect a stronger "international relations" view than the present symposium. Certainly, more meetings were planned to discuss the population problems of different countries and cultural areas of the world. A rapid growth in the underdeveloped countries (although this is a term not used widely if at all in 1948) had suggested a possible increase in world tensions. It was assumed, then, that as these countries developed there would be greater demands for the world's resources, and this in turn would lead to greater tensions.

The development of these "have-not" countries is even more rapid today than in 1948. If the assumption widely accepted in 1948 is true, the tensions ought now to be increasing more rapidly than then. But there are new factors in the present situation which were not known earlier. The ideological factor is recognized now as being more important than certain others.

Nonetheless, since some erstwhile underdeveloped countries will be using increased amounts of minerals and power — India and China being outstanding examples — it is reassuring to note that in the present discussions the problem of technology will be fully treated. We must show a concern for the use of the world's resources; I suspect they will play an even larger part in the world's international problems

127

than they have in the past. I admit a special interest here — after all, I wrote a book on it thirty or so years ago. [Editor's note: His book was *World Danger Spots*, which in 1929 effectively predicted the rampage Italy, Germany, and Japan were to embark on.]

In a way, the 1948 Minnesota symposium on world population problems stressed the cultural aspect more than the current one. There is, perhaps, not as high an interest today as in 1948. Then four sessions were devoted to discussions of causes of birth rate growth; in the present meetings, only one session is devoted to "culture." It is quite likely, moreover, that if we were to give more space to "culture" it would not be in the same channel as in 1948. I suspect that there would be an emphasis on factors of economic development, if I can read the implications of the program correctly.

I note that the genetic aspect of population problems will be discussed. This is a matter of prime concern to be welcomed by laymen. Most non-experts are bewildered when they must make policy decisions that involve genetic variables — for example, regarding "natural" and "accidental" radiation.

It is encouraging to observe a group of men, trained in diverse aspects of science, gathered to consider how they can work together on population problems. This seems to imply that there is an organic component of a total environment which holds to a reciprocal relation of man to nature. If I am right in believing this, then I must regard the coming discussions as a long step in the right direction.

PROFESSOR WHELPTON had illustrated part of his argument with what had been called the "demographic revolution." This is at least an empirically true statement of what happened in much of the industrialized West, when the death rates declined before the birth rates did. The difference between the two — the lag, if you will, of the decline in birth rates — permitted population growth.

The two rates may be drawn as arithmetic curves. When plotted on the same graph, a striking difference appears. But Robert Cook, director of the Population Reference Bureau, suggested an important limitation. While the curves describe what actually happened in history, one ought not treat these curves as *natural laws*.

It would be possible to make a "smooth" mathematical curve, and one could intellectually fondle the equations. These would relate birth and death rates to historical time. But to assume that all societies must pass through similar curves would be an overgeneralization. Dr. Whelpton pointed out that he intended these as illustrations to facilitate an acceptance of the basic idea. At the same time, he acknowledged Dr. Cook's point: overgeneralization can lead to incorrect expectations.

Here we see an important force at work in the world of science: the attempt to secure precisely stated mathematical arguments. These have the strength of our best logic; but, being precise, are easily shown to be false if they are false. Hence, the need to protect oneself from overgeneralization.

Although few in the audience could hold themselves to be experts in the subject matter of Ancel Keys' paper, some interesting sidelights, especially from a sociological point of view, were brought out during the discussion.

Research has shown a sex and social class linkage to certain "modern" causes of death like heart disease. The linkage is explained through an analysis of the relation between diet and heart disease — for diet is indeed to a large extent a function of social class. And so is the other aspect of heart disease — tension. Moreover, tension being related to the amount of cholesterol in the blood, the fact that the male lives in a more competitive world than the female shows some connection with his greater likelihood of having a coronary thrombosis.

Something of a surprise, I think, is the fact that the kind of research reported here indicates the theoretical limitation of a germ or virus theory of disease. Not that the germ theory is shown to be wrong; rather one needs to know not only the relation between germs and viruses and man's life potential (clearly related to culture through "public health" and so on) but also anything that impinges on the biochemical processes. If certain ways of life generate disturbing neural processes, then the "causes" of these disturbances must be taken into account. A new kind of integration seems to be required: even in areas long regarded as belonging to "medical science" the sociologist finds it possible to make a contribution.

Professors Broek and Deevey treated a fairly well related subject: the relation of man to his geographic environment. Dr. Broek showed how certain earlier ideas of a man-land ratio were too simple to be fruitful. Indeed, the data involving "density of population" contained some rather puzzling contradictions. The puzzle disappeared, it will be recalled, when one understood how much the "density of population" failed to take into account. The type of farming in, say, certain parts of China would generate a higher density ratio than that found in some cities in America.

Dr. Deevey went on to a more general point: if we look at biological specimens other than man we find that at some point in a fixed system of food supply a balance between food and population is achieved. He suggested that something similar takes place in the case of man.

Dr. Philip M. Raup of the University of Minnesota presented cogent comments on these points and others.

Philip M. Raup:

One impressive argument that emerges from these papers concerns the unrealistic nature of equilibrium concepts in population study, particularly in any static concept of an "optimum" population. This emerges with especial clarity from Dr. Deevey's paper.

The economist, in particular, is struck by the similarity between the concept of a climax situation, in an ecological setting, and the use of "equilibrium" models in classical and neoclassical economic theory.

Especially significant is the similarity between the concept of an oscillating equilibrium in population theory and the concept, for example, of the hog or cattle cycle in economic analysis. The biologist identifies three- or four-year cycles in mice, voles, and lemmings, and ten-year cycles in snowshoe hares, which seem to fluctuate regularly for reasons intrinsic to the system. In the same vein, in the market economies of Western Europe and North America, we seem to have hog and cattle cycles that fluctuate regularly for economic, not biological, reasons intrinsic to the system.

A basic reason for these fluctuations is the lag in stimulus and response. The generating forces in the cycles in lemmings, snowshoe hares, voles, and the like are intrinsic to the system but are biological. The generating forces in the hog and cattle cycles are also intrinsic to the system but are socioeconomic. They are probably more nearly comparable to the type-situations that would characterize the oscillating equilibria of a human population, where the "shifters" in the situation are matters of technological change, consumers' choices, and costs and returns.

Note that Dr. Deevey allows for two kinds of time lag: time needed for an animal to start reproduction when conditions are favorable; and time required for individuals to react to changing density by altering their birth and death rates. This is quite similar to two kinds of time lag that can be distinguished in the study of hog and cattle cycles: biologic lag, due to gestation periods and time required to produce a marketable carcass; and managerial lag, or time required for the production decision-maker to recognize a changed situation, and to act on his new base of expectations.

Presumably a cultural group that sought to adapt its reproduction pattern to a shifting technological base would face somewhat the same problem now faced by farmers in attempting to plan their hog production in the light of our present imperfect knowledge regarding the generating causes of the hog cycle.

In this setting it seems appropriate to suggest that the population specialist may be able to adapt some useful analytical tools already developed by the economists, especially the "cobweb theorem." [1]

The "shifters" that may move the supply and demand curves for human populations, and thus relocate an oscillating equilibrium at new levels, are not automatically called forth by pressure of a population on its food supply. Many students of history have noted that, in a broad sense, necessity appears not to be the mother of invention. Peoples at the subsistence margin do not improvise, or pour forth inventors. Truly oppressed peoples do not revolt. A certain level of development and well-being must be achieved before mankind can afford the investment of capital needed to permit people to think and to experiment. Experimentation is costly, not all experiments turn out successfully, and some margin for error or a shock-absorptive capacity is needed in a system to permit it to adjust to new situations, or to develop new potentials. There should be no reason for complacency about man's ability to devise new solutions to new problems merely by reasoning from analogy based on present rates of progress in some areas of the globe. Say's law (that supply creates its own demand) does not work in reverse, either. A "demand" for food does not necessarily call forth the supply, or ensure that men will find ways to increase it.

[1] See, for example, Mordecai Ezekiel, "The Cobweb Theorem," *Quarterly Journal of Economics*, February 1938; reprinted in *Readings in Business Cycle Theory* (Philadelphia: The Blakiston Company, 1944), pp. 422–42.

The only general definition of "development" that all peoples seem to agree upon is that providing for the reduction of infant mortality rates and the prolongation of human life. This is probably not the aspect that should receive first attention in an underdeveloped country, plagued with problems of population pressure or inadequate food supply. In terms of the effect on food production, increasing life expectancy at age fifteen and after would be much more effective than programs of infant and maternal health. It would seem that programs that aim at lengthening the years of productive contribution to the labor force, and increasing the effectiveness of adult labor, should get first priority.

We have broken away or are on the verge of breaking away from the limitations imposed by the concept of the "natural fertility" of the soil. We see more clearly today than ever before that food production is fundamentally a matter of energy, and of alternative rates and methods of energy conversion.

Dr. Broek shifts our focus to this aspect of the problem when he says that the "great danger of the future lies not so much in the pressure of population on food production, but in the insatiable demands man will make on the industrial resources of the earth." We are increasingly dependent on these industrial resources for our food supply, on the power needed to produce our nitrogen or to make the steel for our farm equipment and refine the fuel to power it.

This should not lead to despair; rather it holds the promise that man may be able to augment the energy system represented by sunlight, rain, and soil in ways that will enormously increase our food-producing potential. In the past we have consistently underestimated the rate of technological advance. At almost any time in the past three hundred years demographers in the Western world could have predicted food shortage, based on estimated population increases and known methods of utilization of food-producing resources.

Our concept of the world as a big globule of resources, floating unused through space until man came along and "discovered" it in successive bits and pieces, is contrary to all that we know of the history of plant and animal life. It betrays a fundamental misunderstanding of the nature of a "resource." There are no "resources" until man is there to use them, and knows how to use them. What is "man"? What is "land"? Dr. Broek raised these questions but he did not answer them.

132

It seems impossible to define a resource without some parallel concept of "man," and man changes. In the process of changing we men are continually discovering new ways to use resources, i.e., we are continually inventing new "resources," and are rapidly increasing the rate of redefinition of our resources. Our ability in this direction often outruns our ability to organize the distribution and utilization of these resources. Here is the crucial problem: that of organizing our political and social behavior so that we can make maximum utilization of the techniques and resources at our disposal.

Where are the big increases in food production in the near future likely to come from? From the already developed food-producing lands. There is a "snowballing" effect in the application of brains and capital to the production of food. It takes a long time to get the snowball rolling, but in much of the world this process has only just begun.

We have, then, the technical capacity to bring populations into balance with resources and technology. The principal barrier is the cultural one. Our current life expectancy in the United States at birth is about 70 years. As Samuel Brody has pointed out: "The reproduction rate in man — its biological mechanisms and supporting traditions (including religious) — were evolved to maintain the species in an era when life expectancy was 14 years." [2] These traditions make it virtuous to prolong life but not to prevent conception. Until we can reconcile these conflicting cultural patterns we must expect to continue to face the problem of serious food shortages in significantly large areas of the world.

Biblical history is full of allusions to food scarcity, to droughts and famines. Visions of the good life, of the promised land, have been full of references to agricultural richness, to lands of milk and honey, and to well-watered plains. Parts of the Bible can be read as a great textbook in agriculture and in land economics. This is particularly true of the Old Testament. We read these accounts of the early days of the Christian era as a part of the cultural history of the Western world. But we in the United States do not identify ourselves with these problems. Famine is not a specter that haunts us. Drought means economic suffering but it does not mean death to us. I doubt that anyone in this symposium has ever known true hunger.

[2] Samuel Brody, "Facts, Fables, and Fallacies on Feeding the World Population," *Federation Proceedings*, Vol. II, No. 3 (September 1952), p. 689.

For many people in the world today, however, the Old Testament accounts of the struggle for food are timely. Parables of lean and fat years are terribly real. Famine is more than a word; hunger is a known sensation. It has been estimated that half the world goes to bed hungry.

The technological advances of the past two centuries have widened the gap between those for whom hunger is only a word and those who know it as a reality. Not only is the gap widened but more and more people are becoming aware of it. Knowledge of how other people live is rapidly penetrating into the most remote parts of the world. Modern communications, and two world wars in one generation, have thrown in sharp contrast the gulf that separates those who eat well and those who eat badly, when they eat at all.

Much more important is the fact that those who know famine and hunger are beginning to realize that famine is not the scourge of their gods, and that hunger need not be.

At the other extreme we have nations that are plagued with problems of surpluses which they cannot market at home and cannot dump abroad without seriously affecting world trade relations. This is the setting in which we must examine the current interest in world food problems.

A balance between population and food supply involves doing all we can to increase food production while striving at the same time for a recognition of the need for a more rational approach toward population policy.

Bringing population into balance with food supply has come about gradually and more or less unconsciously in the Western world. Birth rates have fallen as people have sought gradually for higher levels of living for themselves and their children. They have sought better education, better housing, higher standards of dress, more leisure time, and more of the material comforts that have become one generation's luxuries and the necessities of their children. This has led to an emphasis on quality of the population and not simply on quantity.

Dr. Broek's concern with the problem of industrial raw material supply provides us with an appropriate setting in which to view the problems of food supply for the modern world. There is no real difference between pressure of population on food supply and pressure on industrial resources. They are one and the same problem.

It is this realization that affords us ground for a cautious optimism.

The atomic age gives a new meaning to the aphorism knowledge is power. To this we can add that energy is food, the limits to knowledge seem infinite, and the growth curve appears to be logarithmic. The focus on population problems in the atomic age shifts from a concern with the physical limits of food supply to the cultural, economic, and social barriers to population balance. The quantitative aspects of the problem recede, the qualitative ones assume new prominence.

MAN is a biological creature. Not only must we concern ourselves with his needs for mere survival. We need to know whether traditionally desired capacities are being continued, or whether undesired characteristics are being passed on to the next generation. In short, we may raise a question of biological *quality*, as against quantity.

For an academic generation, the Jukes and the Kallikaks have been silenced. The environmentalists have had their day. Too often, it would seem, any argument regarding genetic influences on behavior took on a political tinge: biological inheritance can sound like a racist doctrine. But this is poor logic. While a racist doctrine requires a strict biological argument, awareness of the biological limits to behavior does not imply a racist position. At any rate, a world war against a Nazi doctrine of racial supremacy seems to have frightened into silence those who look at the genetic foundation of idiocy.

Today, however, a new fear has emerged: we fear genetic mutation because of radiation. Is this fear warranted? What, indeed, are the present theories regarding the genetic future of man? It was to this type of question that Karl Sax addressed himself. And, in general, speaking as a geneticist, he gave a straightforward answer. His discussant, Sheldon Reed, also a geneticist, is director of the University of Minnesota's Dight Institute for Human Genetics.

Sheldon Reed:

Every professor can remember some one of his teachers who developed a whole new field of interest for him, perhaps in a single lecture lasting less than an hour. My eyes were opened for the first time to the problems posed by population growth in just this way by Karl Sax, one of my professors at Harvard University. I have never forgotten this one lecture, which astounded me. This was in the 1930s and hardly anyone was aware that the United States would ever need to be concerned with overpopulation. After all, the birth rate had been falling for some years and many economists thought that more babies would pull us out of the depression. Consequently, the generalization that some parts of the world were already overpopulated did *not* attract favorable attention. In those days anyone who had a serious interest in Malthus could expect to become an object of derision. I suppose that, since Pollyanna is much more comforting than Cassandra, few of my fellow students took Professor Sax's serious lecture very seriously.

How times have changed! Today, everyone knows that Asia is overpopulated, including the politicians of India who hope to relieve their situation in an aesthetically acceptable and humane fashion. Even in the United States the wild fluctuations of our birth rate are being scrutinized, partly because of their disruptive effects upon our educational system: this birth rate change is manifest in part by a critical shortage of teachers and schools which will get a good deal worse before it gets better.

The considerable fluctuations in the birth rate in this country in the last twenty-five years are not due to biological changes in the fertility of the population but to changes in attitudes toward reproduction. It is clear that in any modernized country the birth rate responds to the will of the people and to nothing else. Hitler and Mussolini were quite unsuccessful in their attempts to force the birth rate up in their countries and the saintly Mr. Gandhi apparently failed to sell abstinence to very many Indians. The changes in attitudes toward reproduction come about as a result of everyday pressures and not as a direct result of the exhortations of those in positions of authority.

I am not straying from my field but am insisting that in any country the *civilized* inhabitants can and do control their own reproduction, at least within broad limits, and do so as a result of the pressures acting upon their own families. Almost every young couple wants one or more children and if they have failed to produce any after some years they may adopt one or more, or sometimes their infertility may contribute to a divorce. About one third of the infertile couples may be helped at an infertility clinic such as we have at the University of Minnesota and may later produce children.

Roughly one out of every fifty couples at some time produces a child with a gross mental or physical defect. In all cases this is a source of grief to them and something which they would have preferred not to have happened. Many of the most responsible of these parents come to the Dight Institute and other heredity clinics throughout the country to find out what the chances are that a subsequent pregnancy would result in a repetition of the same abnormality. Such parents can usually be told that the chances of a repetition are significantly lower than they had assumed them to be. They are thus encouraged to have more children than they had thought wise. The successes of the infertility clinics and the heredity clinics in stepping up reproduction are, then, *in a sense dysgenic* in that they increase the spread of whatever heredity may be involved in the infertility or the specific abnormality for which the counseling was given. However, the infertility clinics and the heredity clinics are *eugenic* in that they also increase whatever heredity is present for the commendable sense of responsibility and compassion shown by the couples who come to these clinics. It is not now possible to decide whether, genetically speaking, the dysgenic effects are balanced by the eugenic gains or not. Both kinds of clinics certainly help to preserve marriage and the family, and thus sociologically are of obvious value. It is reasonable to expect that with our continuing increase in knowledge in the science of human genetics we will be able to give genetic education in the future that will also be more effective eugenically.

My final and most important point is that eugenic improvement as needed for modern conditions will only occur in societies where the birth rate responds rather precisely to social needs. In overpopulated countries, where an equilibrium is maintained by the Malthusian checks of famine and large-scale disasters, the birth rate does not respond to social needs and eugenic attitudes and behavior are nonexistent. Until the *quantity* of people in a given area is adjusted at a social level which permits literacy, no intelligent improvement of the *quality* of the population, either genetic or environmental, can be expected. An oversimplified statement of the eugenic hypothesis could be that life in our society is more satisfactory than it was in cave-man days, that we don't want retreats in reason to those times, and finally, that we think life can be improved by genetic selection of the future man.

UP TO this point the symposium had centered on man as a peculiar type of object. It was as though things happened to man, and certain consequences obtained. Man had biological needs for sustenance. If these were to be met, certain kinds of productivity had to be developed. Man had a relation to space—the material world around him. An iron-consuming man like "Americanus" had a different geographical need than "Africanus," though the latter seemed to be getting more and more similar to the former. Flies adapted their birth patterns to their food supply — and the growth curves of many societies had a rather obvious similarity.

But certain clues were dropped along the way: not man-in-relation-to-land, but how man used his material world. Not merely producing things for consumption, but how these things were distributed. At times some arguments seemed to require a rational man — or at least a core of rational men to plan a whole new world. These suggestions generate doubts. And finally it dawns on us: man is man. He is that peculiar being who can be an object to himself — he can be both the subject and the predicate of a simple sentence. He sees the world — his geography, his friends, and himself. Moreover, he has that which we call culture.

It was to the anthropologist that the task of seeing population in respect to culture fell. Robert Spencer, acting head of the University of Minnesota's Department of Anthropology, presented this topic. A colleague of Professor Spencer's, Alex Weingrod, commented on the paper. Observe how Mr. Weingrod proceeds by restating the argument and then adding his own contribution by making precise some of the earlier statements.

Alex Weingrod:

It seems to me that we really know very little about the problems of population. Whatever the terms in which we put the questions — physical, biological, cultural — we are typically met, I suggest, by varying degrees of ignorance rather than solid knowledge. Not only have we no answers, we have only begun to ask the first questions. It is probable that, for a variety of reasons, our lack of understanding is greatest in the "cultural realm." Here we literally grope in the dark. Published studies on the relation of "culture" and "population" are almost nonexistent. Moreover, in those rare instances in which controlled research has been attempted, the data have often either been presented within a rather limited framework — the so-called social-structural — or are based upon such highly particular and special samples that one is loath to draw large-scale generalizations. To use the metaphor of this symposium, it may be that the area is a fertile one, but progeny are hardly in view.

Now this rather dim situation places severe restrictions upon anyone addressing himself to the problem. It seems to me that what Professor Spencer has therefore done is to say what one would expect of an anthropologist; in effect, he has presented the "anthropological viewpoint." Now I would suggest that there is very great merit in doing exactly this, in suggesting what the implications of anthropological theory and research are for the relationships of "culture" and "population." Essentially the question then becomes this: if we know but little of the specifics of the real situation, what good guesses might be made on the basis of our more more sophisticated understanding of the nature and dynamics of culture?

In this light, it seems to me that Dr. Spencer has ably represented the anthropological tradition. He provides us with both an approach to the problem and some possible key relationships; in a sense, he asks the first questions.

I would suggest that his paper may be summarized in terms of five general propositions:

1. If our problem is to understand the great variations in population, then answers will probably be in the realm of the cultural, not the biological.

2. It is useful to relate population shifts to their ecologic setting; more general historic factors, however, tend to rule ecologic potentialities.

3. Different cultures have taken markedly different positions in regard to population; these are to be understood primarily in terms of cultural norms or values, and only secondarily in terms of structural arrangements.

4. There may be an important correlation between populations and civilization. Large population aggregates may be a precondition of civilization; marginal population areas are also marginal culture areas.

5. The intrusion of one culture upon another sometimes has the effect of disturbing life to the extent that the "will to live" diminishes; this is seen most recently in the contact of Western industrial societies with non-Western pre-industrial groups.

I hope this listing has not done an injustice to Dr. Spencer's intentions. I would like to discuss these points briefly.

The entire bent of recent anthropological tradition suggests that we may best understand population variations in cultural rather than biological terms. Yet at the same time, we must at least entertain the possibility of biologic effects upon the fertility of different communities. Our understanding of human genetics is at best modest. We therefore cannot rule out the possibility that different population aggregates may have different genetic potentialities and that these affect fertility. Lorimer has urged this point rather strongly; "we have no basis," he argues, "for an assumption that all human populations have approximately the same genetic capacity for reproduction." In the absence of sound evidence, we must admit the possibility of genetic effects.

Moreover, there is the further possibility that diet, disease, nutrition, and a host of related factors may influence fertility. Again, our knowledge is far from adequate. Lacking evidence, we can only urge a rigorous examination of the problem, and in the absence of conclusions, leave the biological door open and accessible.

Professor Spencer's stress upon the ecologic foundations of human living is well taken. It may be that we stand here on somewhat firmer ground. Kroeber and Steward, among other anthropologists, have usefully explored the effects of ecology upon culture. What is now called for is a closer study of a variety of human situations. For example, we still lack substantial information regarding so-called nomadic peoples. In what sense does nomadism by definition restrict population? Is such restriction universal to all nomadic peoples? If there are variations, what factors may account for differences? If we now intensively examine these situations, then this "living laboratory" may provide some very useful generalizations.

I can only second Spencer's position in emphasizing "culture" rather than "social structure" in relation to population differences. While it is sometimes argued that particular social structures *in themselves* affect population, the argument is far from convincing. This position maintains that certain kinds of corporate kinship groups — unilineal lineages — promote population growth. When we ask why this should be, there is no firm answer, only the statement that the larger the corporate group, the more powerful it becomes. Now this argument must rest upon at least two assumptions: first, that a corporate group has some being beyond that of its constituents, and that this being is decisive; and, second, that such a being finds it "good" to be powerful. Since neither of these assumptions is seriously defended, and since it is certainly difficult to impute "being" to a lineage, we must call the entire enterprise into doubt. In fact, when pressed hard, structuralists often fall back upon notions such as "joy and pride" of the parents in explaining population growth. And it seems to me that this is the proper position from which to proceed – namely, the attitudes and premises inherent in the culture itself.

If we turn then to the various cultures, it will be useful, I suggest, to separate carefully different types. If we imagine the situation to be one of industrial versus pre-industrial communities, we will encounter serious difficulties. Certainly there are varieties of industrial settings. Similarly, "pre-industrial" masks a variety of significantly different situations. A village in rural India, long established within Hindu civilization, is likely to have markedly different views on population from a neighboring non-Hindu, tribal community. We will thus be in gross error if we imagine our world to be made up of people "like us" and those "unlike us"; in both instances, there are crucial distinctions we must be mindful of.

Although Professor Spencer's paper is largely directed at outlining the effects of "culture" upon "population" shifts, this formulation might be reversed: one might ask, what are the effects of "population" upon "culture"? In examining this relationship, he follows the lead of Childe and Steward in arguing that civilization, wherever it has occurred, has appeared in conjunction with a significant rise in population. Certainly the evidence from both the New and the Old World appears convincing in this regard. However, we might ask, among other things, whether this has always occurred: has civilization emerged in all those instances where sedentary agriculture and large populations have been present for long periods? Now here the answer is probably in the negative. In the case of Africa, we have had agriculture and urban aggregates for probably a thousand years without the development of civilization. Thus we may conclude that while population size may be a necessary requisite of civilization, it is not a sufficient cause. Population may affect the genesis of civilization; but it certainly will not determine its flowering.

Finally, we have the question of the impact of one culture upon another, and the tragic image of a "dying culture." Certainly such devastating results have come from the contact of our own civilization upon others. Yet we might pause to imagine another possibility — that the intrusion of Western civilization sometimes provides a helpful model for a desired reconstruction of the native society. We have traditionally imagined pre-literate communities to be functionally related, pleasing enterprises. There may be situations, however, in which cultures, while functionally related, may in truth be unhappy places; in such a case Western civilization may provide a useful path out of the structural trap. Certainly this seems to be the case among the people of Manus that Margaret Mead has recently re-described. Among them, the impact of the West led not to despair, but to a reorganization of life that seems pleasing to the population. Thus while such an intrusion is often devastating, it may also be truly enriching. Culture as well as population may grow under a sudden, yet desirable, reordering. How this will affect population is certainly not predictable. But we may anticipate growth as well as decline.

FROM Mr. Weingrod's discussion we can more clearly appreciate how a theoretical analysis develops some cogent issues that are researchable. Observe the particular wording in that last sentence: "issues that are researchable." Many people, layman and expert alike, are prone to turn away from "mere theorizing," as though there were something wrong with the attempt to get at fundamentals. Of course, no one really objects to such efforts. But the layman intuitively rejects what the expert precisely formulates: those theories which cannot be tested and hence are "not researchable." If the truth of a statement cannot be tested, we feel psychologically insecure. Therefore, when "theory" is restated in such a way as to permit a rigorous test, we are happier with the theory.

A different reaction to "theorizing" is apparent in the comments which Dr. Thompson directed toward Professor Harberger's paper. Professor Harberger is an economist, though with a varied background in scientific inquiry. He began his paper by arguing against a Malthusian position. Malthus had argued that, unless certain "positive checks" occurred, man would outstrip his food supply. By developing a mathematical model, Dr. Harberger was able to provide some possible conditions under which the Malthusian doctrine of gloom would not be so apparent.

Dr. Thompson, in commenting on Harberger's paper, announced himself as a neo-Malthusian but said he did not wish to carry further the argument regarding Malthus and his theory. It is interesting to speculate on what lines of thought would have developed had the discussion continued to center on Malthus. The point that Malthus was a better seventeenth-century psychologist than a twentieth-century sociologist would probably have been made. But Dr. Thompson chose a more fruitful line of thought: the practical problems involved in the application of any theoretical solution of the "population problem."

He began by arguing with Harberger's concern for growing "capital" in the areas characterized by impoverishment. Now "capital" is not an easily understood word. We all have some idea that it means "money"; most of us agree that it is not "spending money," but "investing money." In particular, "capital" often refers to the "produced means of production" — factory equipment and the like. Dr. Thompson suggested that, in the case of countries like India, "capital" should be modified to include education and the basic utilities. Unless there is a segment of the population capable of manning the factory, there is little need to "pour" capital into an area.

Indeed, he asserted, there can be a danger that overcapitalization will increase the difficulties. With increased capitalization, each worker becomes highly productive; and to produce a given amount of purchasable goods, fewer workers will be needed. Hence, there is some defense for the maintenance of a cottage system of production. This is pretty much like the system of production in England during the seventeenth century, when the spinners and weavers of cloth worked in their own homes.

But "capital" ought also to include the basic utilities of electricity and transportation. In order for a culture to develop a "machine economy," these latter two are prerequisites; indeed, their absence contradicts the possibility of there being a "machine economy."

With these considerations, Dr. Thompson outlined some fundamental difficulties in the capitalization of the impoverished countries. To facilitate the discussion, he used only "rounded approximations," since carrying a precise decimal point would not clarify the argument.

About three fourths of the world's population are in such a condition that they spend almost 80 per cent of their income on food alone. After meeting other costs of living — shelter, clothes, etc. — there is very little to be saved. What little can be saved must be used to replace their existing capital inventory. A farmer knows his bullock will die some day; he must save enough to buy a new one. The hoe will some-day wear out, and it, too, must be replaced. To a horrible degree, this just about exhausts the ability of most peoples to develop a capital reserve.

It has been estimated that a society must put 1 ½ per cent of its cap-ital valuation in reserve for *replacement*, instead of adding it to the in-ventory of capital goods. Moreover, in order to sustain a 1 per cent increase in population, there must be a 3 to 4 per cent increase in capi-tal equipment. If this is added to the amount needed to secure adequate replacement, there should be a 5 or 6 per cent savings for capital goods for a 1 per cent increase in population.

Recently, India has had a very favorable increase in agricultural production. Not all of this is "real": only about 20 per cent of the gain is due to improved agriculture. The rest is apparently due to the highly favorable monsoons of the last five or six years. As a matter of fact, there has been no crop failure due to unfavorable monsoons during the last "five-year plan"; hence not all the gains can be attributed to care-ful planning.

The problem of extending our knowledge of production is not a simple one. The anthropologist is right: there are various cultural im-pediments to the acceptance of an American middle-class ideology. Suppose that, in the 700,000 villages in India, 100,000 of them have agricultural extension agents. This does not mean that these 100,000 villages have modern agriculture. The difficulty can be illustrated from an experience that falls within the personal knowledge of Dr. Thomp-son.

An attempt was made to get a highly successful farmer in India to buy some hybrid corn and plant it. It was known that, in America, if the successful farmer adopts a new practice, others will soon tag along. The same scheme was tried out in India. But in India there is a prob-lem of replacing one's capital goods out of meager savings. This means that one must save a sufficient amount of seed to replant in the next season. To ensure a cultural defense of such savings, a tradition was built up that it is a disgrace to have to buy seed in the planting season.

If you were so improvident as to be unable to save sufficient seed, you were not a good farmer. Hence, it would be a disgrace to buy seed.

The successful farmer knew quite well that hybrid corn would be a better investment than the corn previously used since it could double the productivity of the soil. But he also knew that if he bought corn to plant, he would lose status. He was already successful; he would rather not risk his social position. He did not wish public disgrace.

Now, are the Indians "silly," "irrational"? Is culture "merely getting in the way"? Not at all. We too follow our cultural valuations. These selfsame difficulties are discovered when we study how American farmers change their farming practices. This is the way of culture: it binds and limits man. Even our "rational" culture has its limits: Is a person really capable of understanding national and international issues simply by surviving to age 21? Is a person really no longer productive because he has reached age 65?

In addition, Dr. Thompson warned, India is not a homogeneous population. Some villages prize adaptations, while others resist. The cultural values are not the same throughout the country. There is incredible variation. The techniques which secure adoption of some device to increase capitalization in one place may fail in another. Continued research in this area is clearly needed.

Dr. Harberger asserted that there was really very little difference between the position of Dr. Thompson and that advanced in his paper. He admitted some arithmetic difficulties with his equation (it could approach infinity under some conditions), but these are not serious. As a matter of fact, he said, even admitting all the difficulties Dr. Thompson pointed out, the world can support a bigger population than it does now. One of the troubles is that the situations of impoverished countries are not all the same. Right after World War II, Germany was an impoverished country — but not in the same sense as is India. For one thing, Germany has a cultural tradition and a cultural basis for investment. In that sense, Germany was a good deal better off than the objective data would indicate: its people were culturally prepared to advance.

Some countries have totalitarian governments which impose no purse-string checks on decisions; policy decisions are made by "boards" and not by the "market." It is not altogether clear just how such decisions are effective. Certainly, they can "force" capitalization. And

The Population Ahead

China for one has been charged with indifference to the death rate because there are too many people to care for as it is. If, after a high death rate has aided the task of forced savings, the government can turn attention to public health, it will have a propaganda tool at its command. It certainly does not have the same regard for human life that is motivating our concern for impoverished people. Perhaps under a materialist ideology one can manipulate the death rate to the favor of capitalization; certainly no humanistically oriented society would be able to do so.

Other countries, like India, Dr. Harberger continued, are "half and half." There is some allocation of capital investment through a bad market, and some through a plan. This, he said, involves a misunderstanding of capital. India would materially benefit from the plowing of 20 per cent of its national income into investments, since it needs a capitalization beyond replacement of current materials and the needs for an increased population if its "standard of living is to be increased." This means, roughly, the need of about a 20 per cent interest rate on invested capital. In turn, this means that India would need a "double return" in five years — 5 times 20 per cent equals 100 per cent to be needed beyond the amount of capital invested. It is in this context that a high death rate becomes a feasible way of control — provided that the "state" and not the survivors "inherit" the "fair share" of this forced savings; except for the initial investment in funerals, the cost of "upkeep" for the dead is minimal. The "interest" could be returned completely for reinvestment with no big demands upon consumption. Conversely, lowering the death rates could result in an increased demand upon the savings.

From the floor, certain observations were made. Sheldon Reed commented on the success of the introduction of hybrid corn into Mexico. He continued by showing how a genetic theory can assist in solving some of the problems facing a highly populated world.

Others raised this question: suppose the impoverished become jealous of us, become fearful of the rate at which we are consuming the earth's materials; suppose they band together to take what they feel is rightfully theirs? Ought we not now put a part of our resources to their assistance? Do we not have a responsibility, to our own future if not to the rest of the world, to lead in the research for better utilization of the limited materials of the world? Must we not continue sociological and anthropological research into the problems of assisting countries to assist themselves? The consensus seemed to be an affirmative answer to these rhetorical questions.

Robert Cook made some comments on the awareness of the population problem. He likened population growth to the situation of a skier who, after accelerating on a downhill slide, ran out of snow. The skier had an accident. The world population growth, too, has been accelerating; and, Dr. Cook asserted, "We seem to be running out of snow." The countries bordering the Mediterranean and in North Africa seem to be experiencing a 3 per cent population growth. Where will this lead? With the rapid exploitation of resources called for by a modern standard of living, the crisis comes ever closer. Apparently, we must rule migration out as a solution, at least in the near future.

On the other hand, there is an increasing awareness of the problem. As recently as 1947 there was no formal recognition of a demographic problem, no apparent need for a policy. Certainly, Minnesota's first symposium on population did not share the awareness manifest in the 1956 meeting. But during the interim some changes have taken place. Not only are the professional demographers concerned, but an ever-increasing number of intelligent lay people are studying the problems connected with population. Japan has already shown an official awareness of the problem. A change seems imminent in Egypt. The Roman Catholic Church is seeking an answer to the problem within the morality it recognizes. India is concerned with the problem; and, apparently, Communist China has some awareness that communism does not solve these problems, whatever Marx may have written.

This makes for interesting possibilities. The speculations which would follow from these might add to the fund of questions to which we seek answers. In any event, the population problem does not exist by itself. It is only analytically separable from other considerations. Countries seeking a huge war machine take one attitude toward a rising population. Countries with a Christian ethic take another. And so it goes. But at least awareness of a problem seems to be increasingly general. And with this awareness, perhaps, comes a greater likelihood of solution.

Dwight Minnich, head of the University of Minnesota Department of Zoology, chaired the final session. In a brief summarization, he made the following observations.

The Population Ahead

Dwight Minnich:

If this speaker has any place on this program, it is as a representative of that large group of biologists who, while claiming no especial competence in the field of population, have always had a deep and abiding interest in the subject. In the long lean years before the current increase of interest, they have kept insisting that the qualitative and quantitative aspects of human population were basic to all other human problems.

It is now eight years since the first symposium on human population problems was sponsored on this campus by the Minnesota Human Genetics League and the Center for Continuation Study. Those years have witnessed a colossal change of interest in this subject. That symposium was still a rather faint voice crying in the wilderness. The mere mention of Malthus was still unfashionable, and the suggestion of population limitation by any attempt to control the birth rate had to be approached obliquely, to say the least.

In the intervening years, that climate has completely changed. From every quarter, voices which carry authority in the fields of biology, of sociology, of economics, of government, and of religion have begun to emphasize the increasingly critical nature of human population problems. For despite the understandable timidity of the demographer to predict in view of the complexity of the variables involved, and of the anthropologist even to define population, the number of people in the world continues to expand at an ever more alarming rate.

Dr. Deevey's careful calculations of the base of support for the pyramid which culminates in human protoplasm is indeed a challenging one. That pyramid has a very finite base. And one may ask with propriety, who wants to live on water hyacinth or algae, much less on purely synthetic foods, should the chemist, with unlimited nuclear energy, be able to synthesize sugar, fat, and amino acid?

Nor is this possible food prospect all. As Spengler pointed out in his article, "Production Threatens Prosperity," in the *Harvard Business Review* a year ago: "Of even greater importance is the fact that continuation of population growth is likely to intensify various social and economic problems, solutions to which will be sought largely through state intervention. Should this come to pass, the economy will become less flexible and the freedom of individuals to do as they please would tend to become highly circumscribed. In this event, the stork would

148

have managed to do what the followers of Marx had found themselves unable to do for all they tried — fasten fetters on mankind." Surely we must focus attention on keeping rate of population growth commensurate with rate of production in any approach to the quantitative aspect of population planning.

Dr. Sax has called attention to the insidious problem of defective genes. Not only are we here confronted with the multiplication of the spectacularly undesirable genes, but even more important the possible general downgrading of the whole pattern of desirable inheritance both physical and mental in populations. What a critical matter that also is for peoples who believe in democracy and aspire to remain free!

I believe the basic purpose of this symposium is the same as that of the first symposium of eight years ago: to bring to bear the opinions of experts in various fields on three questions:

1. Is the human population of the earth growing at a rate which threatens the standard of living which most of the individuals in that population aspire to?

2. Is the genetic composition of the population or any significant segment of it tending in directions which are deleterious to the common interest?

3. If the answer to either 1 or 2 is yes, what, if anything, could and should be done?

To me, the answer to question 1 by this group appears to be a rather emphatic yes, although we differ somewhat as to time scale, and as to whether the equilibrium toward which the total world population tends is to be of an oscillating or a more stable type.

To be sure, Dr. Keys, as he surveys the world's diet, seems sanguine that we can feed another 600 million, but Dr. Whelpton estimates that in another decade or so at our present rate of production we will have increased world population by this much. Nor is it certain that by that time we will have effected the mechanization, the curbing of overeating, and the reduction of spoilage and waste which are necessary to save this amount of food which is now lost.

Dr. Broek points to the increasingly rapid expenditure of the earth's nonrenewable resources and pertinently asks, How long can this go on? That technological advances and better planning can and may provide for considerably larger numbers of mankind seems clear. But there is a limit not only in the food but in the space requirement of the individual which most of us certainly would deem minimal. The concern of more and more people around the globe with respect to this matter would appear, from this symposium, not to be without justification.

As for the second question, the possibility of deleterious changes in mankind's general genetic composition, it would seem highly desirable if large-scale sampling could be made at rather regular intervals to determine if indeed any such change is taking place.

For the third question, I think we would agree that an indispensable part of any solution to both the quantitative and qualitative problems of population must be in some regulation of birth rates. As Dr. Spencer has pointed out, we are here on the delicate and difficult ground of varying traditions and attitudes of different peoples toward fertility. Nevertheless, working within the framework of existing mores, ways must be found when necessary to exercise some control. Meanwhile, as Dr. Sax has so wisely observed, we must educate mightily to alter many of these mores and folkways to facilitate a more modern approach to these problems.

I believe the time is not far distant when at national and international levels some form of population planning will become more and more imperative.

In conclusion, I should like to cite two paragraphs which may be familiar:

"The great and unlooked for discoveries that have taken place of late years in science; the increasing diffusion of general knowledge from the extension of the art of printing; the ardent and unshackled spirit of inquiry that prevails throughout the lettered, and even unlettered, world; the new and extraordinary lights that have been thrown on political subjects, which dazzle, and astonish the understanding; and particularly that tremendous phenomenon in the political horizon the Russian revolution, which like a blazing comet, seems destined either to inspire with fresh life and vigour, or to scorch up and destroy the shrinking inhabitants of the earth, have all concurred to lead many able men into the opinion, that we were touching on a period big with the most important changes, changes that would in some measure be decisive of the future fate of mankind.

"It has been said, that the great question is now at issue, whether man shall henceforth start forwards with accelerated velocity towards illimitable, and hitherto unconceived improvement; or be condemned to a perpetual oscillation between happiness and misery, and after every effort remain still at an immeasurable distance from the wished-for goal."

In case there should be any doubt, these are the opening paragraphs of Malthus' "Essay on the Principle of Population," written in 1798. I have taken the liberty of substituting two words in the first paragraph, science for natural philosophy and Russian for French.

INDEX

Index

Ceylon, 55, 126
Childe, V. Gordon, 102, 141
Chile, 15, 118, 121
China, 58, 101, 102, 103, 130, 145: rate of population growth, 18; problem of birth rates, 25-26; optimum size, 42-43; arable land, 55; family in, 105; Western influence on population expansion, 106; birth control in, 127; concern with population problem, 147
Chitty, D., 83, 84
Cholera, 36
Christian, J. J., 83
Christian Era, 13, 88, 133
Clarke, J. R., 83
"Cobweb theorem," 131
Collotheca gracilipes, 75
Communists, and population problems, 18, 42, 127
Contraception, 19, 25, 46, 103, 127
Cook, Robert, 128, 129, 147
Copper, supplies of, 42, 113, 114
Creamer, Daniel, 120
Culture: definition of, 7, 98; as link between man and land, 53; attitudes toward population, 98-99, 103; variability in, 99-100; relation to other factors, 100-1, 139; and ecological patterns in society, 101-2, 140; social structures and population, 102-3, 106, 140-41; defining a population, 103-5; attitudes toward reproduction, 105; norms and population, 106-7; and population balance, 133; effects of population on, 141; interrelations between cultures, 142

Dall, mountain sheep, 78-79
Daphnia, 72-74, 76, 84, 86
Darwin, Charles, 64
Davis, David, 91
Dawson, Walker, 91
Death rates, 25, 43, 95, 126-27, 145, 146: during demographic revolution, 13-14; in United States, 14-15, 43; in Middle and South America, 15, 19; in Europe, 15-16, 17; in Asia, 16, 18-19; in Africa, 18; interaction with birth rates, 71; in primitive society, 87
De Castro, Dr. Josué, 37-39
Deevey, Edward S., 129, 130, 148
Demographic revolution, 13-19, 26, 128
Demography and demographers, 9, 40, 64, 76, 86, 103, 125, 132, 147, 148
Density of population: in world, 53; corresponds to climatic regions, 54-55; op-

timal increase, 70-71; effect on mortality, 72-73; and birth and death rates, 84-85; apparent contradictions in data, 129-30
Dickens, Charles, 43
Diet, *see* Calories; Food needs
Dight Institute for Human Genetics, 137
Diseases: and food shortage, 36; and survival, 87; control of, 126; limitation of theory of, 129; and fertility, 140
Drosophila, 73
Dublin, L. I., 72
Dysgenic effects, 137

Ecology and ecologists, 71, 75, 76, 84, 101, 102, 140
Economics and economists, 4, 9, 10, 130, 136, 142, 148: contribution to population study, 7-8
Education, effect of birth rate on, 136
Egypt, 18, 42, 54, 70, 72, 147
Emlen, J. T., Jr., 81
Energy balance, statics of, 70
Environment: and heredity, 8, 90-91; man influenced by, 87; unfavorable, 89; effect of control of, 91, 94; improvement needed in social, 96-97; and socio-cultural factors, 100-1
Equilibrium population, 130-32: definition, 64; and productivity, 64-71; and longevity, 71-79; aggression, anxiety, and natality, 79-84; oscillation, 84-86. *See also* Optimum population; Population growth
Eskimo, 103, 104
Europe, 6, 13: population growth in, 15-16, 17; calorie shortage during war, 32, 34; density, 54; arable land, 57; productivity of land, 57
Ezekiel, Mordecai, 131

Family size: in United States, 21-25; income pressure on, 109-10
Far East, 37
Fertility, 17, 25
Florida, 68
Florida Keys, 67
Floscularia Edmondson, 75
Folkways, 150
Food and Agricultural Organization (U.N.), 55
Food needs: estimate of calories, 28-29; effects of technological advance on, 29-31; by occupation, 30-31; specific nutrients, 31-34

Proteins in diet, 31–32, and reproduction, 37–38
Public health programs, and death rates, 25
Puerto Rico, arable land in, 57

Racism, 135
Radiation, 128: effects of, 8, 91–94, 96, 135
Rates, *see* Population growth; Natural increase of population, rates of
Raup, Philip M., 130
Raw materials, *see* Natural resources
Ray, J., 84
Reed, Sheldon, 135, 146
Religion, attitude toward population problem, 95, 147, 148
Reproductive practices: effect of undernutrition, 37–39; varying, 105–6; barrier to population balance, 133; changes in attitudes toward, 136. *See also* Birth control
Roman Catholic Church, and demographic problem, 147
Roman Empire, 102
Rome, 73, 103

Sankaran, Dr. G., 32
Sargassum, 75
Sauer, Carl O., 62
Sauvy, Alfred, 40
Sax, Karl, 135, 136, 149, 150
Say's law, 131
Schroeder, H., 66
Science, limitations of, 10
Scott, J. P., 82
Selye, H., 82, 83
Sex, effect on caloric needs, 29–30
Sickle cell gene, and environmental conditions, 90
Singapore, population increase in, 16
Slonaker, J. R., 38
Social class, relation to length of life, 6
Society, definition of, 7
Sociology and sociologists, 9, 10, 71: contribution to population study, 7
South America: population growth in, 15, 17, 19; agricultural land per farm worker, 58
Southeast Asia: population growth in, 18; vitamin deficiency in, 32; density, 54; productivity of land in, 57, 58
Southwick, C. H., 81
Spain, arable land in, 57
Spencer, Robert, 138–41, 150

Spengler, J., 148
Spirorbis, 74
State Institute of Human Genetics (Sweden), 89
Steel, consumption of, 8, 59
Stern, Curt, 92, 93
Steward, 140, 141
Strecker, R. L., 80, 81
Subsistence, minimum, definition, 27. *See also* Subsistence level
Subsistence level: and health, 32–33, 34–37; and strength, 35; and political stability, 35; and reproduction, 37–39
Süssmilch, 27
Sweden, 52, 89, 94, 111
Switzerland, 57, 111

Technology, 149: effects on caloric needs, 29–31, 39; effects on nutrients, 31–32; and natural resources, 63, 113, 127, 132; and increase in agricultural output, 108–9, 110–11; components of advance in, 118–19; limits on advance, 119–20; differences among industries, 120–21; rates of advance, 121; in underdeveloped countries, 123
Temperature, effect on caloric needs, 28–29
Thailand, 52
Thomas, William L., 62
Thompson, Warren S., 125, 142, 143, 144, 145
Tribolium, 73
Trobriand Islanders, 105
Tuberculosis, and undernutrition, 36
Turkey, 90
Typhus, 36

Underdeveloped countries: and Malthusian pressure, 111–12; model of economy, 116, 117; difficulty of achieving efficient production in, 119–20; need for technological progress, 122–23; and control of diseases, 126; in *1948* and *1957*, 127; need for increasing adult labor, 132
Undernutrition: in wartime, 34–36; effect on reproduction, 34, 37–39; and tuberculosis, 36; effect on children, 36–37; emotional effects, 36–37
Union of South Africa, demographic revolution in, 18
Union of Soviet Socialist Republics: population growth in, 15, 17, 18; arable land in, 57

United Kingdom: arable land in, 57; rate of technological advance in, 121

United Nations, 18, 28, 29, 59

United Nations Educational, Social, and Cultural Organization, 106, 107

United States: population growth in, 15, 17, 20–25; migration to, 20; size of family in, 21–25; relation of nutrition to health in, 33; proteins in diet, 39; density of population, 53, 70; arable land in, 55; productivity of land, 58; and welfare of individual, 62; differential birth rates, 88–89; attitude toward family, 105–6; materials consumption in, 112–13; model of economy, 116–17; productivity of capital in, 117; rate of technological advance in, 120, 121

Utricularia, 75

Vitamin shortages, 31–32, 37

Völkerwanderungen, 102

Wangersky, P. J., 85

West Germany, 57, 118, 121, 145

Western culture, 98, 99, 107

Weingrod, Alex, 138, 142

Whelpton, Pascal K., 128, 129, 149

Wisconsin, University of, mouse experiment at, 80–81

World War I, 120, 126

World War II, 21, 25, 32, 34, 36, 37, 121, 145

Zimmerman, Erich W., 53